About the au

Ian is a bipedal great ape belonging to the species *Homo sapiens*. Like all great apes he has a curved spine, no tail and opposable thumbs. Unlike most great apes he is equally happy on land and in water. Whilst Ian has developed reasonable communication skills his tool making abilities remain poor.

BAD APE

Ian Kerr

BAD APE

Vanguard Press

VANGUARD PAPERBACK

© Copyright 2022
Ian Kerr

A CIP catalogue record for this title is
available from the British Library.

ISBN 978-1-80016-151-1

*Vanguard Press is an imprint of
Pegasus Elliot MacKenzie Publishers Ltd.*
www.pegasuspublishers.com

First Published in 2022

**Vanguard Press
Sheraton House Castle Park
Cambridge England**

Printed & Bound in Great Britain

Dedication

To Amelia and Oscar, two really great apes.

Introduction

Micha was nine years old when she first met Toby.

Already by then, she had shown herself to be fiercely intelligent, kind, funny and strong enough to pull both your arms out of their sockets. Seriously, she could have dragged you through the bars of her cage and snapped you in two if she had wanted to. Fortunately, she hardly ever felt like doing this.

Micha is a Pan Troglodyte, a western Chimpanzee and had lived with her family at the Wonderful World of Wildlife Zoo and Entertainment Park, in the heart of Kent for almost five years.

Before we go any further, there are some things that you need to know about chimpanzees in general and Micha in particular. Firstly, chimpanzees (don't call them chimps, they don't like that) are members of the great ape family that includes orangutans, gorillas, chimpanzees, bonobos and us, sapiens.

There's also one golden rule that Toby learned right from the start — you do NOT, ever, call Micha a monkey. She is a great ape, a chimpanzee, or if you are feeling all formal, a hominid. Apes are not now and never will be monkeys. If you get this wrong, you are prone to see a side of her that you do not want to see and she does not want to show you.

The first, and only, time that Toby made that mistake she fixed him with a withering stare and an outrageous simian sneer to let me know just how dumb she thought he was. What she did next, however, was to change Toby's world forever and maybe the rest of the planet as well.

Chapter 1
The Zoo

The move to the zoo had gone perfectly.

Working with a fleet of removal trucks and an army of removal men Dan, Alice, and Toby Potter had gone from living the London high life to being residents in their own private zoo in less than two days.

The move had come as a response to Alice finally getting the all clear from the oncology department. Dan had sold his business for an almost unimaginably large fortune and the three of them had decided on a new life as far removed as possible from the glass-palace London penthouse that they had been living for all of Toby's young life.

Their new home was Hartfield House, an eighteenth-century stately home that stood at the centre of the grounds of the Wonderful World of Wildlife Zoo and Park close to the East Kent coastline.

The Potters first saw the house together as they drove through the imposing double arch cast iron gates that opened on to the sweeping half-mile gravel driveway. The private road took them up the hill to the front steps of the twenty-seven-roomed sandstone mansion that towered over the park like it was keeping watch over all that lay beneath it. Toby had sat with his face pressed against the car window, eyes wide and shooting from side to side as he tried to take in the enormity of what surrounded him.

The driveway was lined either side with beech trees planted close enough to each other so that their branches joined to form one continuous canopy stretched over its entire eight hundred metre length. Beyond the trees lay perfectly tended lawns that could fit ten football pitches on either side and still have room for the spectators. At the end of the drive was the central car park that surrounded a twenty-metre pond which formed an oasis in a desert of gravel. In the middle of the pond stood a huge willow tree on a central island offering shade to the fish and birds that lived in and around it.

In the centre of the house's vast facade were three marble steps that invited guests up to the colossal oak doors which opened into the Grand Hall.

The drive up to the house must have taken no more than thirty seconds, but it felt to Toby like he had journeyed all the way from one life into another. His whole time in London had always left him feeling like he was an outsider a confused bystander caught up in a game he didn't understand or want to be part of. Their glass walled apartment, quarter of a kilometre off the ground may have cost more than half a dozen zoos but Alice had nicknamed it the Fishbowl Flat and the comment had always made Toby feel like he was an exhibit stuck in a show case. His father, Dan Potter, had grown up living hand to mouth in a no-go zone just north of Tower Hamlets. Toby's mum, Alice, by comparison had grown up well off, but only on a scale that never rose above half broke. Dan and Alice were perfect together but they hadn't ever fitted into the world of air kisses and lattes-for-lunch that Dan's phenomenal head for figures and assassin like ruthlessness for trading had landed them in. Toby had picked up on this sense of not quite belonging from as early as he could remember and no matter how palatial his glass palace was, it still felt like a display case to him.

Here in the park, though, Toby suddenly felt completely and utterly at home. It was as though the iron gates at the foot of the drive marked the end and the beginning of his two lives while the oak doors of the house greeted him like the open arms of an adoring grandmother.

The Potter's car swept around the pond and pulled up in front of the steps, but Toby was out of the car before the wheels had stopped turning. He pushed open both of the front doors and ran the length of the Grand Hall shouting "We're home! We're home! We're finally home." It was twenty minutes before he stopped running by which time, he had visited every room at least twice but had not even noticed the entrance to the cellar or the patio doors at the back that opened on to the zoo itself.

The next three weeks passed in a delirious blur of excitement and exploration with Toby unstoppable in his quest to cover every square inch of the grounds that surrounded him. The past year of his Mum's illness and those endless days of sitting by her bed willing her to eat even just one corner of a slice of toast were a distant memory. He wasn't even sure that they were his memories. It was as though he was remembering a film he had watched once, the details hazy and confused, like images viewed through murky waters.

By the end of the first week, he had met all of the team who worked at the zoo and had been shown every animal that lived there.

Suddenly tedious science lessons spent talking about mammals, reptiles and birds were transformed into days spent getting to meet the big cats, the monkeys and lemurs, the penguins and the giant tortoises, crocodiles and snakes all of whom were loved and cared for by the fantastic Natalie Brooker, Head Zookeeper, and her band of part-time helpers.

Uncle Jack, Alice's brother had joined them mid-afternoon of their first day in the house. Toby had grabbed him by his hand and dragged him out into the zoo, desperate to share with him the explosion of new experiences that Hartfield House and grounds were showering him with.

Jack Friday was just as excited as Toby. His enormous gap-toothed grin that was never far from his face and sometimes threatened to split it in two was like a gleaming canyon running from ear to ear when he saw his nephew running to meet him. Jack was six feet three in his socks and broad as a barn door. He was quick to scoop Toby up and carry him under his arm, rugby ball style as they leapt from the patio and into the zoo grounds. Jack was bursting to tell Toby his news and blurted it out as they ran towards the big cat enclosure, crossing the back lawn to reach it.

"Toby, guess what? Your dad is my new boss! I just signed on as the zoo's Chief Veterinary Officer. No more part time Peter for me, I will be coming here every day; we are going to be able to do this as often as we want."

Toby's life had just become perfect. In those few words, the past eleven years had become some extended sit in a waiting room, all the while getting ready for this moment. His core began to tighten as a sense of purpose gripped him; he was here for a reason, and he could not wait to find out what it was.

His mum was well, his dad was going to be home every evening for tea, he was going to see Uncle Jack almost every day, and he had his own personal zoo to fill every waking moment.

And for a brief glorious moment that is precisely how it was.

Jack was true to his word and was in the zoo every day and if it bothered him having a Toby shaped shadow with him at all times, he certainly never showed it. Together they explored every square metre of their new domain with Toby learning about his surroundings from all who worked there.

The zoo was spread out over sixty acres and was divided into four zones. The Jungle (primates, monkeys and big cats), The Birds (one enormous aviary), The Polar Zone (penguins and sea lions) and The Reptile House.

Toby learned from the older members of the team how part of the zoo's quirkier charm was down to the previous owner, Half Baked Hal, lead singer for last of The Lost Souls, the last of the 70s great super groups. In his time with them, he had enjoyed enormous fame and success touring America for almost twenty years, a career pathway that had left him in recovery for the following thirty years. His considerable wealth and limited self-restraint allowed him to make rash career decisions like creating extravagant follies in the woods that surrounded the park and building a state-of-the-art ape house, the largest in the country that sat empty for five years before the zoo could attract a single ape to come and live in it. By the time the Potters took over though, it was the star attraction and represented Hal's most significant achievement at the zoo.

The success of the ape house was due almost

entirely to the efforts of Natalie Brooker, the head zookeeper, who had been running the place on a day-to-day basis for the previous five years.

After the Potters took over the zoo, Jack and Natalie, who had worked together on and off for a couple years, could now work full time, day and night writing up plans to develop the care and breeding programs for the animals. The animals were getting fed and exercised better than ever before, and it was already beginning to show in their behaviour.

And it wasn't just the animals in the zoo that were finding new energy. Toby was erupting out of his old self and morphing into a vibrant, happy, confident eleven-year-old who after just two weeks knew the Latin name of every inhabitant in the zoo along with the first names of all of the team who worked there.

He would strut around the park just out of Jack and Natalie's shadow calling out to animal and human alike, asking how they were and wishing them all well. He had a smile to rival Jack's Alice now, and he was wearing it with pride. His life couldn't get any better.

Then one morning, Alice got a nosebleed.

Chapter 2
A Mother's Love

It was Jack who found Alice. He had popped back into
the main house to pick up some charts he had left on the
kitchen table and found her slumped in the sink, barely
conscious with blood pouring from her nose. He knew
immediately what was wrong and had Alice in the car
rushing to the hospital before he had had time to think
of Dan or worry about where Toby might be.

Jack got Alice to the Accident and Emergency of
the local hospital in less than twenty minutes and was
telling the doctor in charge what to do as he walked
through the doors, forgetting for a moment that this was
a hospital for humans, not animals. It was clear straight
away to Jack and to the doctors in the hospital once they
knew her medical history that her bone marrow had not
survived the ravages of the chemotherapy the year
before. It had lost its ability to make enough blood cells,
and her organs were shutting down because of it. The
nosebleed was a sign that her blood was not clotting as
it should and was mirrored by similar bleeds internally
as well.

She was taken straight from A &E to the Intensive

Care Unit where they started to pump fluids into her to keep her from going into shock while they waited for the blood test results.

By the time they had matched Alice's blood group and got her blood counts back from the lab she had lost consciousness and was lying in passive surrender to the medical maelstrom that was happening around her. It had been barely two hours since Jack had found her in the kitchen but he realised that he had not spoken to Dan or Toby yet and knew that he needed to get them here fast. He made it back to the zoo quicker than he had got to the hospital and ran through the park entrance and into the house where he found them both sitting in Dan's office arguing over the best names for the new mandrill that was arriving at the zoo next week. They were laughing and happy just as they had been for the past couple of months, but all that changed the moment they saw Jack's face.

"It's Alice, she's in hospital. Get in the car, and I'll take you there now."

Dan and Toby didn't ask why or make any effort to resist, they simply rushed out of the house, following Jack in mute obedience.

Both stayed silent, for the next few minutes as if a thousand questions that they had between them were log-jammed in their heads, fighting to get out but too frightened for what they might hear when they were finally released.

Jack spoke first.

"I found her bleeding in the kitchen a couple of hours ago and took her straight to the hospital; I didn't have time to come and find you or wait for an ambulance. She is in intensive care, and the doctors are doing all they can but she's hypovolaemic, her haematocrit is down, she is severely neutropenic, and her thrombocyte count is off the chart."

"Speak English for God's sake, Jack."

"Sorry, sorry Dan; I'm not thinking straight. She has lost a lot of blood, and the blood that she has left is not doing what it should. She has not been making the right amount of white blood cells for months, and her red cells are not forming properly. She can't form a blood clot or fight infection properly, and she is not able to carry enough oxygen around her body to keep her conscious. They were giving her a transfusion when I left so she will have improved for now but clearly. she has been unwell for a few months, and my guess is that her bone marrow was weakened by all the treatment last year. She is very weak right now, but you know how tough she was last year, she can get through this as well. Don't worry Toby; this is your mum we're talking about remember. What does she say? She's a warrior; cancer is more scared of her than she is of it."

It was a good line, and Alice used to say it to Toby each night when there was treatment planned for the next day. She used to hold both his hands, look straight into his eyes and squeeze her fingers tight into his, emphasising each word with a tug on their grip like she was testing a knot. Toby used to look down at their tightly bound fists and love that he could not make out which were his fingers, and which were hers. He had believed it then, and he was clinging to that belief now, gripping his hands together now as if she was there with him.

Dan had listened to what Jack had said and was trying to understand. Alice had been well for months ; she had responded like Toby to the move, like someone had plugged her in and flicked the switch. They had been going for longer and longer walks each day around the park, and Alice had even started swimming once a week. Her appetite was back, and some of her old clothes had started to fit again. They had begun to plan a summer party in the park and were going to invite all their friends, so they could renew their wedding vows in front of them. For the first time in over a year, they believed they would have a future together. Finally, he spoke.

"Did I do this Jack? Did I push her too 'ard, trying to get her well again? Did I make her sick?"

"Of course not. No one ever pushed Alice anywhere she didn't want to go, and even her GP said she was looking good when he saw her last time. How had she been over the past week or so?"

"She said she felt tired last night, but that is nothing

new; I told her to go to bed and get some rest, didn't think anything of it. She didn't go swimming this week and hadn't wanted to do our walk yesterday, but I thought she was just mad at me for forgetting it was your mum's birthday on Sunday, I was supposed to get her tickets for the Rod Stewart concert next month."

"It's Mum's birthday on Sunday? Seriously? No one told me."

"You're worse than me Jack. Alice is right you got the brains, but she got the 'art."

"Alice has brains to spare as well, more than she ever gives herself credit for. She will have known something was wrong, but I guess that things reached a tipping point in the last two or three days. Her blood counts will have suddenly dropped off a cliff, and she won't have known what hit her. But that heart and brain of hers will get her through this. Don't doubt me guys, Alice will rally round the moment she sees you."

At least Jack was right about this. Within an hour of getting to the hospital and sitting by her bed, with Dan whispering in her ear, Alice opened her eyes and managed a thin, watery smile. She squeezed Toby's hand in their usual way and used the other to wipe a tear from his cheek. She was too weak to talk, but these little actions told Toby all he needed to know; she loved him and was still strong, still fighting.

Dan kissed her head and stroked her hair all the while locked in an unbreakable eye contact that seemed almost physical in the way it bound them together; like it was telling the cancer that it would have to take them both on.

"'Ello, beautiful. What have you been up to? Anything to get out of a walk, eh?"

Alice smiled again. She knew what Dan was really saying "I am terrified; I thought I had lost you."

As soon as the doctors saw that Alice was awake, they stepped in and asked Dan and Toby to give them a minute while they chatted with her. Before either could protest, Jack had wrapped his arms around them both and steered them to the door knowing that a painful conversation was coming and certain that Alice would want to hear it first before Dan and Toby had to suffer it. Toby held on for one last reassuring squeeze of the hand, but even he knew that he had to cut the tie, if only for a moment.

She stayed in her hospital bed for just over a fortnight, fighting every second from one breath to the next. By the end, her skeletal frame lacked the weight to leave even a dent in her pillows, but her fiery red hair lay across them as if to form a halo around her, a defiant beacon of hope against the final onslaught.

It was her immune system that let her down in the end, almost any bacteria or virus could have beaten her defences. A partially washed hand or a polite cough might have delivered the final blow but whatever it was the battle was over in forty-eight hours. Alice was completely overrun with infection and her heart and lungs could not keep up with the huge demand this put upon her. The speed of it all caught even the experienced ICU team by surprise, but Alice had given them explicit instructions before the event, just in case. She had told them, "Enough. I am tired; I can't keep fighting and keep giving my boys false hope. If the time comes just let me go, at least they will be spared any more of seeing me like this. Maybe that way they can remember me as I was, not as I am."

Dan and Toby had barely left the hospital in the whole two weeks she had been there, and Jack had been coming down before and after work each day, so at least they were all there when the crash finally came. They could see the lights begin to dim on the morning of her last day and knew by early afternoon that they had a few hours, at most, left with her. Toby had climbed into bed next to her and was squeezing her hands as tight as he dared. Dan was unable to sit down and was pacing the room thinking frantically of some untried strategy or new plan that would bring her back from the edge. His short squat frame and hunched over shoulders gave him the look of prize fighter stalking the ring. H was clicking his thumbnail against his front teeth which showed the world he was thinking, don't disturb him. He had grown used to the machinery that surrounded Alice and knew what the oxygen saturation and blood pressure and heart rate should be; he could see the numbers falling like a countdown timer, could feel the seconds slipping by to the point where his life with Alice was going to end.

Their life together was the only life that mattered to him. They had met when he was fifteen, he was forty-three now. He had been with her for two-thirds of his life. He was not much older than Toby was now when they met. Any life before her was a life of learning to ride a bike, kicking a football in the park, and getting into scraps with his older brothers; he didn't know how to be an adult without Alice by his side.

When it happened, it was as if she knew. Knew it was time to surrender, time to let go for one final time. She called out for Dan and grasped Toby with what little strength was left in her atrophied muscles. With one defiant last breath, her lungs emptied and made no attempt to fill again. In unison, the machines all reached their final deadly alarm call, and the thin red line went flat. Breath had become air, and life had become cold flesh.

Toby clung on to her neck and squeezed her chest as if trying to encourage one last breath, one more attempt at life. His tears didn't come straight away, but when they did, they were great rivers of grief flowing down his cheeks and soaking into her hair. His sobs racked his body, convulsing him into breathless, soundless cries of pain, strings of saliva hanging shamelessly from his mouth.

Dan looked on, each eye a fathomless well of

sadness. The fretting and pacing stopped, the urgency gone from him like a boxer who has heard the count and knows there is no point in trying to get up any more.

Jack had entered the room for the last few moments but had stayed by the door, alone in his grief, unable to help and sickened by the thought. Alice had been his safety net growing up; she had kept him grounded when his brains and his looks threatened to engulf him. She had supported him at every turn, been his compass when he was lost. She was the barometer he used to test the world around him, but now all he could do was stand in silent despair, his words gagged by grief, as she left his world forever.

Chapter 3
Ash and Dust

Alice Potter died on June 23rd, 2011, three months to the day since they had moved into the zoo and one month shy of Toby's twelfth birthday.

The weeks that followed stretched into years and shrank back into seconds with every passing hour. The bereavement nurse had told Dan that the most important thing for Toby was not to break his routine and should carry on going to school as usual. Dan had thanked her for her advice and ignored every word of it, leaving them to huddle together like castaways in a raft, alone on a shoreless sea of grief.

He and Toby had shrunk in on themselves and had retreated to the small cottage that sat to the side of the main house and was nicknamed 'The West Wing.' The main house had started to accommodate Alice's and Dan's extended family and, nearer the date of the funeral, the caterers and guests who had travelled down from London and needed somewhere to stay. Neither Dan nor Toby wanted to spend one minute longer with them than they had to so The West Wing offered the perfect haven for them, with Jack and Natalie the only two aliens allowed to entire their private universe.

The day of the funeral saw over two hundred friends, family, and zoo workers attend. The service took place at eleven a.m. in the church just down the road from Hartfield House with a priest that Alice had never met giving a speech about the life of someone he had never known. After the service, the immediate family followed her coffin to the crematorium while the remaining guests walked the few hundred yards back to the park to begin the wake.

By the time Dan, Jack, Toby, and his grandparents were back from the crematorium the wake had begun to concentrate around the caterer's marquee, the guests using a mouth full of food as an excuse for not speaking, not saying what they were really feeling. The low hum of murmurings and chewing fell to silence as the family entered the tent, an awkward, clammy silence that almost dared someone to break it.

Inevitably it was Jack who spoke first. "Come on guys, this is not the sort of party Alice would have wanted; it's a free bar for god's sake, let me buy you all a drink!"

It wasn't much of a speech, but it gave everyone permission to smile and talk and let their guard down enough to allow a few real emotions to surface.

The guests stayed all afternoon and into the early evening but by sundown, almost as though a whistle had blown, they all started to make polite excuses and look for their coats. Sensing that wake was ending Dan took a step up on to the makeshift stage at the end of the tent and took a piece of paper from his pocket.

Everyone in the tent saw what he was doing and turned to face him, silenced once more, waiting for him to say the words that Alice's life deserved, that spoke of the Alice they knew, not the one the priest had tried to sketch so clumsily in the church a few hours previously.

Toby looked on with excruciating anxiety, dreading the words that would be delivered in the past tense to describe his mum.

Dan stood there for what seemed like eternity going into overtime. Toby stared helplessly as his dad stood, head down staring at the scrawled notes on a piece of paper. He was clutching the scrap like a climber holds on to a cliff edge, their life reliant on the strength of their fingertips. His mouth was opening and closing, puppet-like, but the words were cowering at the back of his throat unable to give sound to the thundercloud of anger and sadness and grief and disbelief that was building in his brain, threatening to be spat out like hailstones of bitterness and rage.

Jack started to rise from his seat, ready to step into the void that was engulfing Dan. But with a hand pushing down on his knee, Toby sat him back down as he stepped up to join his dad on the stage.

Toby stood beside his dad, half his size but somehow rising above him. His box fringe of ginger hair hung flat, ashamed almost, against his saddened brow, his slender frame hidden beneath a suit that hung like a cloak around him. Toby held his dad's hand and pulled him close in a way that made onlookers doubt who was the father and who was the son. For a brief moment, Toby scanned the audience, his glacier blue eyes casting a beacon of hope over them as he did. With a voice broken with the physiology of his age but strengthened by the belief of what he was about to say Toby began to speak.

"Don't go, don't leave just yet. Not until I've said what I need to say."

This was almost as many words as Toby had said over the past two weeks and the felt strange in his throat, rough against unused vocal cords. With a swallow though Toby gave the mouth the lubrication it needed, and the words were able to flow out, a continuous stream of emotion flooding out of him as the dam finally burst.

"Everyone here knew my Mum, some of you knew her as a friend or a sister, a daughter or a wife but I am the only one here who knew her as a mum. She was my mum; she made me, she grew and fed me, washed and clothed me. She was the one who made me come to life; I couldn't have existed without her. Only I can remember what she was like when she was being my mum. The way she smiled at me when she was dishing out my food, or how she would dress me in the morning for school or how she took my temperature when I was ill. No one else but me has these memories, and if I ever forget them, then no one in the world will ever know how brilliant she was at being my mum."

The words were flowing fast and easy now, starting to gather pace as if they were becoming aware of the importance of what Toby had to say.

"Every one of you has your memory of her. Your own little, unique piece that can recall her from the day she was born until her last. As we stand together in this tent, this is the last time that all of those memories will come together in one place. Right now, we can all make her whole again, put every piece of memory back together again so that all of us here can know just how amazing she was. The moment we leave, the picture we have of her will break up again, you will each leave with your own jigsaw piece of her, and you must protect it with your life because if you lose it, we will never ever be able to put her completely back together again."

Toby bowed his head slightly as if to show he had finished all that he wanted to say, but just as his father came to put his arm around him, he snapped his head back up and started to speak again. This time though, his eyes that so far had stayed stubbornly dry were now moist with the first tears of the day and his previously strong voice was beginning to falter.

"The energy that held my mum together through all her life has gone now. But at school, we were told you can't create or destroy energy you can only change it. If it is not in her any more, then it must be in us. We were closest to her so we must have trapped that energy as it left her and now it is part of us and will help hold us together throughout our lives. If we all join together then that energy will connect back up, and if we all think of our memories then we can make her whole again; just for one last time."

And with that Toby reached out for his dad's hand and Jack's and they each did the same to those standing closest to them. Within a few seconds, everyone in the marquee had joined hands and moved in tight together, looking around them searching to make eye contact with the those who shared their closest memories. The group held that connection for one, brief, beautiful moment. Then, with no visible signal, they all let go their hands and broke into a spontaneous wave of applause that crested over them, bathing them in a warm rush of energy that seemed to rise up to the peak of the tent and escape into the dark and silent park.

Everyone looked to Toby as they applauded and could see that the fearful, timorous boy who had taken to the stage a few minutes before had become, if not a man, then at least someone who had gained strength and maturity that far exceeded such a few years of age. He had put his arms around his dad's waist, but he had done so not as a young child seeking comfort from a loved one but as someone providing support, offering to take a weight that the other had found too much to bear.

The wake ended with every guest wanting to speak to Toby, to make their promise to treasure their piece of Alice's jigsaw and to keep her energy within them. His words had given them a purpose; they knew what was required of them and what price being a friend of Alice had put on them.

The immediate family members from both sides were staying on in the main house along with some of their closest friends, but Toby did not want to be with them that evening. His speech had taken more out of him that he had let on. Toby had been thinking about those words for the past two weeks, and they had been filling his head, threatening to burst out and any time during that time. He had no idea if they would make any sense to anyone or if he was going to sound like some silly kid that everyone would pity but not really listen to.

For Toby, those thoughts had come to him two days after his mum had passed and had landed fully formed in his mind, uninvited and unexpected like a package delivered to the wrong address. Once he had taken the time to understand them fully, he had known what he was going to have to do at the funeral. The thought of it had left him weak with fear. He was drained from so many sleepless nights worrying about whether he could get everyone to gather as they had done, and whether it would make any difference if he did, that he could not believe it had actually happened.

Once he had got them to join hands, however, he had known without a doubt that it had worked. His memories of his mum had glowed so much brighter in his mind than ever before and his hands burned from the heat of his mum's energy as it cascaded through him.

From the day after she had died Toby had begun to worry that he would not be able to remember everything about her. He understood death and knew he would never see her again for real, but he was sure that he had enough of her trapped inside him always to be able to feel her; but only if he could hold on to all of those memories and emotions that she had left him with.

As everyone else headed back to the house, leaving the marquee as a final, hollow, empty testament to the life of Alice, Toby slipped out through a side door to head back to The West Wing. All he wanted to do was sit, alone in his thoughts and reflect on how his words had affected him.

Natalie Brooker had stayed at the outer edges of the day's events but had watched Toby make his silent exit. She followed a few paces behind him and walked into the lounge just as Toby was sitting down on the corner sofa, a picture of his mum in his hand. He looked up, startled by Natalie's presence, the light and his tired eyes making him mistake her for his mum for one beautiful, then brutal, instant that left him clutching the photo tight to his chest.

He glared at Natalie, cross that she had tricked him into thinking she was his mum, even though he knew she had done nothing wrong and angry that his chance at being alone was going to be taken from him. Natalie met his glare with a forgiving gaze that let him know she knew she was trespassing on his solitude but also showed a quiet confidence that hinted at the possibility of an extraordinary secret being shared.

"No time to sit down Toby, my boy. It's time I took you to meet someone that you are going to want to get to know; she is going to change your life forever."

Chapter 4
Micha Speaks

Toby had not been quick to get off the sofa and follow Natalie that evening.

He liked Natalie and knew that Jack did too, but he was exhausted after such an emotional day. He did not want to see anything new or chat with anyone about how he was feeling, which he suspected was what she had in mind.

Natalie made no attempt to take Toby's hand or put her arm around him like every other guest at the funeral had felt compelled to do, desperate to show compassion and comfort to him but not realising how much they felt like they were suffocating him. Natalie was someone who preferred to watch others from afar, seeing how they behaved to one another, before getting too close.

She watched humans like most of us watch animals in the wild; with a slightly amused curiosity as we try to work out what their strange rituals mean and who is in charge of the whole show. Natalie had watched Toby all day and had seen how he had shrugged off each well-intentioned hug and pulled his hand away from each attempted clasp from a well-meaning mourner. She had been able to see the transition taking place in him as he built up to his speech and how he had left the stage with a strength and understanding that many adults fail to achieve in a whole lifetime. She had seen that he needed clean, fresh air around him with the room to move, not the shackles of an uninvited embrace.

Natalie was a difficult woman not to like and even more difficult not to notice. She was just shy of six feet tall and had spiked electric blue hair that made her look like she was permanently surprised. She had an athletic frame that reflected her early career as an international rower and an effortless enthusiasm that challenged everyone around her to try and put her down, daring them not to share her mood. Most of all though she had an emotional intelligence that matched her academic prowess and allowed her to understand the animals she worked for far more than books and degrees could ever allow someone to.

She had lived at the zoo for the past five years and had not taken a single day's holiday in that time, unable to pull herself away from the animals that had become her children, her patients, her employers, her best friends. It was not that Natalie did not like human company, she did, she was very fond of Jack and was at her happiest when the two of them were knee deep in muck in The Jungle enclosures or wading through The Polar pens. It was just that if she had to choose between the company of either, she would take that of animals at least nine times out of ten.

Because people who knew Natalie well knew how highly she valued the company of animals and how indifferent she seemed to that of humans it was impossible for them not to feel honoured when she chose to spend time with them. Once you coupled this with her infectious and boundless positivity, it was inevitable that Toby was going to get up off his sofa and follow Natalie out into the park.

Natalie led them out through the kitchen and into the night. It was clear she was not taking them on an aimless ramble, as she cut straight across the entrance zone and picked up the pace as soon as they were in the zoo.

Natalie frequently checked behind her to see that Toby was keeping up and making it clear to him with a smile and an encouraging flick of her head that they were not on a public tour but were on a mission to get to what she had in store for him.

Toby had become very familiar with the layout of the zoo so was pretty confident of where they were heading, but he was much less sure why. Natalie took them around the back of the big cats' enclosure from where it was a short walk to the front of the ape house.

The chimpanzees had the largest enclosure in the zoo, and it housed a troop of twenty making it the second largest in the UK and the star attraction of the park.

Toby loved the ape house and tried to spend part of everyday here. The chimpanzee's home was divided into an outdoor arena and an indoor enclosure which the inhabitants were free to roam between day and night.

The outdoor stage was stunning. It had forty-foot-high fences and ceiling mesh that surrounded thirty trees and covered an area the size of half a football pitch that allowed the chimpanzees to move around in their separate groups and make dens and rest on their own as they pleased. It was very much their own territory, and the keepers tried to enter it as little as possible, preferring to let the animals run the forested area as their own domain.

The indoor enclosure offered a very stark contrast, however, giving a harsh reminder to both the chimpanzees and zoo visitors alike that the animals were captive here. It was a faceless concrete slab of a prison block that attempted no hint at a natural habitat for these jungle dwelling primates.

The walls and floor were a seamless sheet of cold grey cement that gave the chimpanzees nothing in the way of crack or finger hold but was perfect for hosing down in the weekly clean up that removed the worst of their least savoury habits and attitudes to home hygiene. The ceiling was made of toughened glass and like the outside arena was forty feet high, so at least the animals could climb their sculptured scaffolding 'trees' up to rest seats and makeshift beds high above the unforgiving floor.

The only way into both sections was through a secure entrance at the back of the enclosure which was guarded by a double door system. Both were locked by electronic key fob and separate combination code with the doors on automatic closing mechanisms and set three metres apart making it impossible for one person to have both doors open at the same. It was a strict zoo rule that no one entered the enclosures of the primates or big cats or crocodiles without a minimum of three keepers present; one to enter, one to guard the outer door and one to stand by ready to hit the alarm buttons if anything should happen. These precautions were strictly enforced by Natalie, so Toby was surprised and alarmed to see Natalie get out her keys and head for the enclosure entrance.

Before she got to the first door and before Toby could begin to question her actions Natalie turned full circle, knelt down to eye level and grabbed both of his shoulders.

"Toby, I know today has been the worst day of your life, and I know you will not be able to think about anything else for a very long time, but I saw you today when you spoke, and I know you are ready for what I am about to show you." She moved her head slightly to the side to ease the mood a little. "Look, there is no easy way for me to tell you what you are about to see and you wouldn't believe me if I did so I'm just going to ask you to wait here while I get someone who has been dying to meet you."

This final comment struck Toby as a pretty weird thing for Natalie to say but he was kind of used to how she talked about the animals, as her friends giving them so many human characteristics that it was impossible to tell which species she was talking about.

It took Natalie only a moment to open the first door and enter the lock zone between the two doors. She knelt down by it and pressed her face to the bars that separated the lock zone from the animals inside and called out.

"Micha, Micha darling, come on over Toby is here and he is ready to meet you."

Ready to meet her was not precisely how Toby was feeling; he was suddenly exhausted and ready to go home to bed.

"Come on Natalie; I'm tired I can see the monkeys in the morning, I just want to go home."

Toby we well aware that the chimpanzees were not monkeys, but he knew that it would wind Natalie up and he wanted her to give up on whatever she was planning so he could close this outer door and head back to the cottage. Just as he had finished speaking, however, when something began to stir. One of the Chimpanzees stood up and rushed over to where Natalie was waiting, using that swaying, bow-legged gait that anon-human primates have when they walk upright.

Micha went straight to Natalie and pressed the palm of her hand up against the bars so that it met flush with Natalie's waiting hand in a perfectly timed 'high five.' She kept on moving past her keeper, letting her hand drop as she did, her eyes focused firmly on Toby, who was now transfixed by the intensity of her stare. Micha pushed herself into the corner of the enclosure so that she was as close to the outer door as she could get and hit him with the words that would change his life forever.

"Don't call me a monkey little No Hair. I'm nobody's monkey. I am Micha the Magnificent, a Great Ape and a Warrior Princess and one day I am going to save the world — don't you forget it."

Toby stood opened mouthed, gaping in disbelief as Micha, strutted away from him then turned to face him and curled her lip back in that outrageous simian sneer that he would get to see many times in the future. He stood for a few moments more until Natalie joined him at the outer door and smiled down at him nodding in shared amazement. Toby held it together for no more than a second before he let out a shrill, terrified scream. He ran, skidding and screaming into the cold night air, heading straight to the sanctuary of The West Wing cottage.

Chapter 5
Micha's First Words

Given the stress of the day, it was inevitable that no one took Toby's hysterical claims of a talking ape too seriously.

When he heard Toby's cries, Dan abandoned the remaining guests in the dining room and rushed to his sobbing son.

"She can talk! Micha, I heard her, she talks. You've got to come, come with me now Dad; please come now, Natalie is there, she'll tell you what happened."

Some of his words made it out of his mouth, but most of them were stuck bouncing around in his head. It didn't matter too much because Dan was not listening to what was being said, he was just glad to see his son crying. He had been worried he had not done enough of that; scared that Toby was keeping everything compressed down inside him, frightened for what might happen when it surfaced. Dan needed to see the tears and was happy the catharsis was finally happening, welcome for the chance to join him in the sweet, bitter release that it brought.

Toby tried to pull away, tried to look his dad in the

eye and tell him what he had seen, but it was useless. Dan was clinging to his son like a drowning man clutching a lifebelt. The more they hugged each other, the less Toby struggled, letting the tears of fright turn to the tears of sadness that he so desperately needed to shed, beginning to doubt what he had seen and question if it had happened at all.

Without breaking the hold, Dan lifted Toby and carried him back to the cottage and into his bedroom. They sat on the bed for a few minutes more, and Toby began to tell his dad again what he had seen but each exacerbated attempt to tell the tale was met with a sympathetic nod and knowing smile.

"We'll go and see her in the morning; she'll still be able to talk then."

Toby's resistance gently weakened to a point where he stopped speaking and let his dad's loving hand guide his head to the pillow where an exhausted sleep was waiting for him.

In the morning Toby woke to find Natalie sat on the end of his bed smiling at him over a mug of the milky syrup that she called tea. Toby was shocked to see her there. Natalie was a regular at the cottage, and she and Jack had had many meetings in the office and over the kitchen table there, but she had never been upstairs before and certainly never in his bedroom.

"Wha…?" Toby started to question.

"No time for idle chat, Toby, we have work to do.

Get yourself sorted and meet at the ape house in twenty minutes. And don't bother telling anyone about what you saw; I have told everyone how I had found you wandering in the zoo last night and had startled you over by the chimpanzee enclosure. I told them that you ran off screaming about a talking ape because you had not seen me when I called out to you. Your dad understands completely; he knows how upset you were."

She could see how angry and hurt Toby was by this. His sense of betrayal was etched deep in his face and looked ready to scar it if it got any deeper.

"I'm sorry Toby, but I told you not to tell anyone about Micha. We have to keep it a secret — for now, at least. If anyone else finds out, we will never see her again. God knows what they will do with her if they take her away, she will spend the rest of her life in a laboratory cage, that's for sure. We can see her for a few minutes this morning before the zoo opens but only if you promise me, again, that you will not tell anyone about this."

It was Natalie's turn to show her feelings and her expression left Toby in no doubt as to how serious she was when she said this. And he knew that she was right. Jack had hinted to Toby a little about the history of the chimpanzees in their care and about how they had been treated before the came to the zoo. It had horrified him and left him certain that he would never let that happen to any of the animals in the zoo.

"What about Jack? Surely he knows?"

"No, Toby, not even Jack. I can't risk telling anyone. It has been my secret for over four years now, but if Jack finds out, he won't be able to keep it secret for four minutes. It is just you and me, kid, and that is how it needs to stay. Either you stay silent, or Micha does; that's the deal."

Toby had no choice, and he knew it. There was no way he was going to miss out on seeing Micha and getting to hear her speak again.

"OK it's a deal," he said half dejected, half elated.

Natalie had given him twenty minutes till their meeting; he was at the ape house in six.

She was only a few steps ahead of him as he turned the corner of the ape house. If Natalie was surprised to see him there so quickly, she didn't show it, choosing instead to offer him the briefest of nods and that knowing half-smile of hers that always suggested that she was at least one step ahead of whoever it was aimed at.

"Right Toby, I need to be strict about some ground rules. Micha is not your pet; she is a wild and dangerous animal who could pull your arm off through that cage of hers. You do not, ever, try to enter the enclosure on your own and you never, ever try and get one of the team to let you in with them. This is a 'you and me' deal only, no one else knows about her and no one will, do you understand me?"

Natalie had locked eyes with Toby and was not letting him drop his gaze or break contact until she had heard that assurance from him again that he was not going to betray her trust.

"I promise, Nats, but you have to fill me in, I mean yesterday a chimp spoke to me, and that means either I'm going mad, or the whole world has changed, forever. Animals can talk? When did this start? How come only we know?"

Natalie could see that she needed to bring Toby up to speed and it was only fair that he knew a little more about Micha's history before he met her formally. But where to begin? Toby already knew some of Micha's family history and how the zoo had saved them all from various terrible situations.

He knew that Micha was the youngest daughter of Sally and Sundance, two apes who formed the main family of the troop at the zoo and that she had an older brother Kianza. He was aware of Sally's brother Butch and how Sundance had taken the alpha male spot from him. Natalie had chatted to him before about the relationships within the troop and the two single females, Daphne and Cindy, and how they fitted into the group dynamic.

Cindy and Daphne came from a circus in eastern Europe where animal acts were still popular with humans, although certainly not with the performing animals.

They were actually two wild-born chimpanzees from the Congo like Sundance and Savannah but had been captured by poachers when they were very young. They had been smuggled out of Africa and sold to the circus before they were three years old and had been kept on their own, orphaned and alone with no contact with another chimpanzee for the next ten years. They had been freed from the circus and their squalid home by a charity that tried to rehouse abused performing animals and had been named after the two ladies who ran the charity.

Cindy, for the most part, liked the company of the younger chimpanzees in her new home and acted as a babysitter most of the time. Daphne, on the other hand, was a dreadful flirt and used her charms to endlessly pit Butch and Sundance against each other in a perpetual power struggle that she alone could control.

Natalie knew that Toby was aware of all this, so she figured she may as well just tell him about Micha's first word.

Natalie started by telling him about how she and Micha had bonded very early on. She admitted that despite her best intentions about keeping contact with the apes to a minimum, it was clear that she found Micha impossible to resist. For her part, Micha seemed smitten with Natalie as well and would take every opportunity to sit at her usual spot by the bars of the indoor enclosure whenever Natalie was nearby.

Gradually, Natalie found herself making excuses to go into the enclosure more and more, and every time she did she would find a little companion by her side or, if she was feeling particularly fearless, on her shoulder.

It was normal for Natalie to talk to all of the animals in her care and she explained to Toby that this is how it had happened.

She had kept up her usual one-sided conversations with all the animals but with Micha in particular. Her chats formed a continuous stream of unanswered questions and descriptions of her days, her nights, her relationships and her favourite foods, books and films. The animals, if they had ever cared to listen, would have known more about Natalie Brooker's life than even her mother did.

Sadly, none of them paid too much attention to what was being said, and none of them bothered to join in; until one of them did.

"It was about six months after they had come to live at the ape house and the best part of five years before you guys arrived that it happened. I was finishing my final rounds of the enclosure and was waffling on as normal, asking the sleeping chimpanzees what they would like for breakfast – 'Bacon and eggs? Omelette and chips? Rice Krispies? Marmite on toast?' – when I felt a gentle tug on my bootlaces and a heard a whispered reply, 'Toast?'"

Chapter 6
Natalie and Micha

Natalie had not, at first, linked the tug on her boots and the little voice asking for toast as both coming from the same animal. Two other residents at the zoo rejoiced in their reputation as being the jokers of the animal kingdom and took great pleasure in tricking humans with their mimicry. Del Boy and Rodney, two South American green parrots had been at the zoo for over ten years and were allowed pretty much a free range to come and go as they pleased. They travelled from pen to pen using their trademark flying-hop that saw them jump from branch to branch across the trees of the park flapping furiously with their cruelly clipped wings that could no longer sustain them for full glorious flight.

Del Boy and Rodney had come to the park from the jungles of Guyana where they had spent their early life soaring above the shores of the Cuyuni River from their perches high in the rainforest canopy. They had been captured and brought to England to supply a pet trade that persisted with the belief that animals like this would be quite happy to see out the rest of their lives sitting on a wooden swing in a cage designed to fit on a coffee table.

Fortunately, they never made it into someone's living room as they were found by customs officers and moved to the Wonderful World Zoo as soon as they could leave quarantine. They were given a generous enclosure which they flatly refused to spend any more than the bare minimum of time in, preferring as they did to roam the park like sentries patrolling their stockade or doctors on a ward round, depending on how the mood took them.

They spent their days moving from enclosure to enclosures, doing their rounds to time their visits with each feeding or cleaning time when scraps would be at their most bountiful and the inhabitants of each pen would be most distracted. Often this meant that their arrivals coincided with those of Natalie which allowed them to hone their mimicry skills and see if they could get her to search in confusion for whoever was calling her from afar. They had perfect the cries of small children looking for lost parents, angry dads shouting at hungry young ones eager for ice cream and, their personal favourite, the fire alarm which never failed to cause startled panic amongst the nearby humans.

Given their track record, it was not surprising that Natalie had first suspected that their trickery lay at the heart of Micha's apparent request for toast.

Her first reaction was to spin around, searching the enclosure for one or both of the prankster parrots who should not have been out at that late hour. Before she could confirm or deny their presence, however, the tug on her boot was repeated, firmer than before, and the request repeated, louder and clearer, with a greater confidence apparent within it.

"Toast?"

Natalie had looked down in time to see Micha staring up at her, a quizzical brow adding emphasis to the clearly formed sounds coming from her mouth. This time Natalie did grasp the enormity of what was happening to her but rather than run from it she was able to embrace the moment, thrilled and honoured that this pivotal event in human and ape existence was happening to her.

For the first time since apes and humans had been one species, they had shared a spoken word together, and she had heard it first. Six million years, at least, had passed since this had happened last and whilst 'Toast' was maybe not the most auspicious word to choose to restart verbal communication Natalie was confident that it would not be the last. She was convinced that she and she alone was best suited to continue this unique and precious conversation.

"What did you say Micha? Did you just ask me for something?" she asked, as she folded her full six-foot frame down to the floor and lay beside the young ape as she reclined in her hay bed.

"Toast? What toast?" With these three words,

Micha had taken the conversation to a whole new level, and Natalie spotted it straight away. She had removed any possibility of this being simple mimicry and raised it to the point of cognition.

Natalie knew that Micha was not the first ape to communicate with humans, of course. Many captive chimpanzees had been taught sign language and could communicate to a level of a primary school child when given simple recognition tasks, but vocal speech had always been considered to be impossible for them. It had also always been an accepted truth that chimpanzees could not initiate enquiries that required an understanding of abstract concepts about things that they had never previously encountered. Micha had not received any training in communication and had never seen toast. To work out the words required to ask a question about it and then to form the words using vocal cords that had evolved over millions of years to make an entirely different range of sounds showed a level of intelligence that had, as yet, never been encountered in any animal, anywhere in the world.

"Toast is food. Humans eat toast." Natalie had instinctively signed the words as she said them, using a modified form of Makaton that is used to help human children with speech difficulties. As she pointed her fingers to her mouth to show the word to "eat" Natalie saw Micha's expression change from inquisition to one of knowing and was delighted to see her nod and begin to rub her tummy.

"Food. Eat. Good" Micha replied as she nodded, and Natalie saw a yearning in her young eyes that made it clear that she was hungry and wanted to eat now.

"Is Micha hungry?" asked Natalie, rubbing her tummy with a clenched fist to emphasise the question in a non-verbal form as well.

"Hungry. Yes. Micha Food."

Micha did not bother with any form of signs this time; she was confident that her words were enough.

Their conversation had started to get a little louder now, and it had disturbed some of the nearby apes who had begun to grunt and bark out warning cries that risked waking the whole troop. Instinctively it seemed that they both knew that they must not risk rousing the others. Natalie raised a single finger to her lips and held it there as she reached behind her and grasped a fruit parcel that was also kept close by to distract any overly inquisitive apes when one of the keepers was in the enclosure. Micha reached out an eager hand and took the parcel which she immediately hid in her hay bed fearful that Kianza or one of the other older males might see it and steal it for themselves.

Natalie had stayed lying by Micha's bed watching her with a transfixed gaze, a mix of wonder and adoration, her mind racing through the events of the last few minutes.

She wasted no time wondering if it was a dream or

some elaborate hoax, Micha was real and was a game-changer for the human race.

The idea of marriage and kids had never held much interest for Natalie, but that night she had discovered what a mother felt when they gazed on their new born child. As Micha munched contentedly on half a mango, staring back at her, eyes full of unasked questions and excitement about the future they would have together, Natalie knew that she would die before she let anyone take Micha from her.

And so, it had been that Natalie and Micha had kept their secret, making sure they spoke only when no other apes or humans were around.

When Half Baked Hal had started renovating the zoo in earnest new office space had become available. Natalie had jumped at the opportunity to take up residence in one of the office buildings in the park as this gave her free access to Micha early in the morning or late at night when the other keepers were not around. For the four years that followed until the Potters arrived to take over the zoo Natalie and Micha had spent every spare moment they could steal, whispering in corners or laughing out loud together depending on how confident they felt about being overheard.

In the beginning, it was clear that Micha was struggling with the sounds required to make human speech and had to cut words short or throw her head back to stretch her vocal cords into new and unfamiliar shapes.

She found 'M' and 'B' sounds especially tricky as they needed her to make a seal with her lips to create the sound and this was a very unusual shape to make with her mouth. Many weeks and months of patient tutoring with Natalie passed before Micha could genuinely be described as being able to speak in what passed for normal sentences. For most of this time, she would limit her thoughts to three or four words that got the gist of her message across, just as a traveller with a basic grasp of a few key phrases would do in a foreign land.

Natalie was able to see right from the start that Micha was learning and using language as every human child has done for the past hundred-thousand years, grasping the meaning of the sounds each time she mastered a new word.

By the end of the first year, Micha had a vocabulary of just over three hundred words that she could use correctly to communicate her basic wishes. By adding extra signs and her rapidly developing body language, Micha was able to ask Natalie about events outside of the enclosure, about the other animals and how her day had gone caring for them.

This was a remarkable step as it showed that Micha could understand things about a world that existed outside of her direct vision. The ape arena offered high perches for the chimpanzees to climb to which gave them views across much of the rest of the Jungle Zone and a little of the Polar Zone, but they could not see the whole of the zoo and certainly could not catch sight of all of the comings and goings of the park. Nevertheless, Micha had evidently built up a mental picture of the areas of the zoo that she could not see and was able to retain this image as she asked Natalie how the snakes were doing in the reptile house or how the giant tortoises were getting on today.

In keeping with most other research programs Natalie had worked with flash cards to build Micha's vocabulary. The introduction of an iPad had made this a much quicker process and one that Micha was much happier to engage with. In all other learning programs, the chimpanzees have always been motivated by treats with each correctly identified new picture or successfully used sign earning a quick snack, but with Micha, this wasn't necessary. She wanted to learn and was continually pushing Natalie to name everything around her that she pointed at or answer her questions about the other keepers or animals around the zoo.

Micha was spending as much time as possible learning how to talk to humans, but she also had to learn how to communicate with her fellow chimpanzees. Through this period of learning with Natalie, Micha was growing into an adult chimpanzee and was having to find her place in Sundance's troop. She remained very close to her mother, Sally and her grandmother, Savannah but was starting to spend more time alone or with her brother, Kianza who had two new playmates of his own. The two new friends were a couple of immature male apes called, Sonny and Fredo, who had been introduced from a Dutch zoo two years ago and were very much in subservience to the older and stronger, Kianza.

By the time the Potters had moved in, there were twenty apes in the enclosure, but the number of male chimpanzees and lack of breeding stock within the troop was beginning to become a problem. Kianza was almost fully mature and with the help of Sonny and Fredo would soon become a threat to Sundance and both chimpanzees knew this; tensions were mounting in the troop and Natalie was concerned that one of the many aggressive displays on either side could have resulted in severe injury if action had not been taken to split them up.

Much as she hated to do it, Natalie was relying more and more on Micha's insights into life in the arena to know who needed to be removed to keep the peace.

Chapter 7
Micha's World

It had been a very tough decision for Natalie to let Toby into her private world.

The years that the two of them had spent together at that first word was uttered had been magical for Natalie.

She and Micha had worked together in secret all that time, and neither had even once confided to any other human or animal in the zoo. They kept their meetings very secretive, making sure they were not being watched as they worked their way through Micha's studies.

It is a shame no one ever saw them as they made a spectacular sight; the slender, near six-foot blue haired human in her usual sweatpants and running top combo looming over the near three-foot short haired ape, still with her slightly pink juvenile face and satellite like ears hanging on every word her teacher spoke.

The progress that Micha had made over this time was simply staggering.

She had a vocabulary of over almost a thousand words but could understand twice as many. She could talk about a whole range of topics from what sort of day Natalie had had to what was happening in the football at the weekend. She knew the names of all of the animals in the park, and she was interested in all of their day to day routines. She had even developed a love of classic romantic literature and would make sure Natalie would read some to her every night.

She understood much about human emotions but could never fully grasp the concept of love and marriage having no idea how any female could ever expect a male to fall in love with them. To be fair, she may not have had the best teacher in Natalie as romance was not something that she invested much energy in either.

By the time Toby met Micha, she and Natalie had spent two to three hours a day, every day for the past four and a half years talking, reading, playing on the iPad and chatting about any and every topic that came up. In the early years, Natalie had been mindful to steer clear of topics of conversation about where the chimpanzees come from and why she lived in a zoo. At first, this had been easy to do as Micha could always be distracted by a new game on the iPad or a fruit treat. As her confidence and vocabulary grew though, it became clear that Micha had worked out that she was on one side of a set of bars and Natalie was on the other and from what she could see Natalie was definitely on the better side.

Of course, Natalie was not Micha's only source of

information about the world beyond the bars as the other chimpanzees in the enclosure all had their versions; some from vague long-ago memories of a world without bars and others from lives of hardship spent as performing puppets in circus tents. Or, worse, kept in sterile, windowless rooms full of humans in whitecoats. Sadly Natalie was blind to these conversation as she, like anyone else who had spent years studying how chimpanzee communicate, had never managed to interpret the complex language of pants, hoots, grunts and shrieks all of which came accompanied by an elaborate pantomime of shrugs, hand gestures and facial expressions.

What seemed to humans to be basic commands and alarm calls is actually a rich and expressive language that allows chimpanzees to discuss all that they have learned and experienced from one generation to the next, allowing them to understand more and more about the world around them. Micha had not shared the secrets of the Chimpanzee language with Natalie, somehow feeling that a human cannot be allowed to know everything about the chimpanzee world; she trusted Natalie more than any other human that she had ever met, but she was still a human.

This was a terrible shame because the version of events that Micha and her family had about how they ended up at the zoo was very different from the sanitised version that Natalie understood to be true.

61

The chimpanzees in Micha's troop came from a very mixed background, and so they had a view of the world that was somehow both wide and blinkered at the same time. The troop's version of life beyond the enclosure reflected their various life journeys' but was dominated by one particular ape's thought more than most. .

Sundance, Micha's father, was an ape of extraordinary strength and power, weighing at least twenty-five kilogrammes more than the average male chimpanzee and standing almost five feet tall when stretched to full height. He dwarfed the other members of his troop and controlled them with an unforgiving menace. His life had been filled with heartache and suffering that left him reluctant to speak of his past but when he did it was with words of bitterness and anger and revenge.

He was born in the jungles of the Congo and lived for the first three years of his life with his family and their troop, unaffected by human interference, as chimpanzees have done there for over a million years.

He was able to develop as all chimpanzees should, learning the ways of the forest and the troop so that he could earn his place in the hunts and maybe one day become an alpha male.

Like all young males, he was raised by his mother and aunties who showed him how to groom his elders and how to find food. They taught him when he could approach the mature males and when he needed to give them a wide birth. From his male peers, he learned how to fight, how to develop much-needed friendships and allies and got to join in the hunt for any neighbouring Colobus monkey foolish enough to stray too close to their territory. On one memorable occasion, he even watched the mature males kill a leopard that had been skulking around the troop trying to pick off one of the babies.

Sadly, even the mighty Congo jungle cannot protect all of its inhabitants from the spread of humans and their impact.

Sundance did not make it to his fourth birthday before a gang of hunters led by a grotesquely scarred warrior came and took him from his mother and father who they shot for trophies. He was abandoned in a nearby village and lived a few miserable months chained to a post in the centre of a ring of huts. Here the local human children taunted and teased him by poking him with sticks and throwing stones at him safe in the knowledge that they were beyond the reach of his short chain that was clipped to the collar around his neck.

The villagers called him Kojo, which means angry one, and the orphaned and traumatised young male spent three months sat by his pole surviving on scraps of fruit thrown to him by the children when they got bored of tormenting him. They had planned to sell him on to one of the groups of poachers who came through the village every few weeks, but none of them wanted him as he had grown too skinny and weak looking.

Just when the villagers had decided that Kojo was better off being used for what little meat he had left a group of research scientists from the National Primate Research Centre, in Atlanta USA, arrived at the village.

Their arrival is probably best described as a mixed blessing. The researchers rescued Kojo from the fear and torment of the village but then locked him in their laboratory where they subjected him to almost twenty years of testing and experiments. Kojo spent two decades in a cage barely big enough for him to stand in. There he was poisoned, electrocuted and subject to medical investigations that shame the name of science. He could have been there for the rest of his life had it not been for a change in the law. Experimentation on primates was outlawed in all but the most extreme cases in America and Kojo, along with many fellow chimpanzees were released into zoos and safari parks around the world.

After a lengthy search Kojo was moved to the grandly titled Planet Ape safari park in south west England, meaning that he had travelled over twenty thousand kilometres since being taken from his home in Congo.

It had taken Kojo many years to adjust to his new home in the safari park. He had learned to associate humans with pain and suffering, his only contact with other chimpanzees being limited to shouts and cries between bars, words of encouragement mixed with rage and disbelief at their torment.

Almost overnight he had found himself released into a wooded park with room to climb and swing and floors where he could make nests from leaves and hay. His muscles were weak at first, and his back doubled over from years of cramped conditions but time and medical care from the workers at the safari park had gradually nursed him back to full strength.

Physically he healed quite quickly but emotionally it took him far longer to recover from his torture, and in some respects he never did. The team at the safari park never gave up on him, though, and worked tirelessly trying to gain his trust and encouraging him to form bonds with other apes. Kojo remembered a little of his life as a free chimp and knew some of what was required of him. But these memories had been diluted and polluted by so many years of abuse that anger so often took over when instinct let him down.

When two new chimpanzees, Butch and Sally were introduced to the safari park it was expected that Butch would take control of the troop and Sally would find a mate.

At first, Butch and Kojo became allies and appeared very close. It did not take the workers at the park long to notice the close companionship that the two apes were developing and even less time to start calling them

Butch and Sundance, meaning that Kojo got a new name to go with his new home and friend.

Sally and Butch were brother and sister and had arrived with their mother, Savannah, who, like Sundance, was wild born and had lived in Congo for the first fifteen years of her life. She was taken from the wild and brought to a zoo in Holland when her part of the jungle was destroyed by human activity. The zoo had cared for her as best they could, and she had become pregnant first with Sally and then Butch. The three of them had lived in the zoo in Holland, part of a small troop, for ten years before being moved to the Planet Ape safari park.

Savannah had been able to teach Sally and Butch about how to behave in the chimpanzee world, and it was obvious they were ready to form a troop of their own when they arrived at the safari park, with Butch as the alpha male.

It was not long into the friendship between Butch and Sundance before it became clear that Sundance and Sally were becoming close. What surprised the staff at the safari park was how Sally, Sundance and Savannah started to form a gang with Butch slowly being pushed out. The humans, who know nothing of how chimpanzees communicate, had no idea that Savannah had become very fond of Sundance, recognising a fellow wild born ape who she could share memories of the jungle with. Sally, for her part, was quick to submit to Sundance and between them, they formed an allegiance that ousted Butch as the alpha and installed Sundance instead.

Sally became pregnant shortly after this and gave birth first to Kianza, a male and then, three years later, to Micha, a slightly underweight and slightly premature female infant who gave no clue of just how magnificent she was going to become.

The troop had, at its core, Sundance and Sally with their offspring of Kianza and Micha. Alongside them, there was Savannah who kept the females in line and organised the hierarchy among them and the infants and Butch who alternated between brooding on the outskirts of the gang and being Sundance's closest friend. Outside of this inner circle were six other apes who fell into line under Sundance's control. The twelve of them existed in a quiet harmony for three years like this as Sundance's mood swings and violent rages became less frequent.

It had been hoped that Sundance and his troop would stay in the Safari Park for many years but, sadly, the decision to introduce a semi-mature male into the park had proved to be disastrous.

Sundance could not accept his presence and from the start attacked the new arrival with increasing ferocity until it became clear that serious injury or death was inevitable if the situation was allowed to continue. Moving Sundance, alone, and leaving a new alpha in charge was not an option as they might well kill Kianza and Micha while Sundance would be very unlikely to settle into any new troop under a new alpha.

So, the decision to move Sundance along with his close gang of Savannah, Butch, Kianza and Micha were taken. It was with great luck that this happened at a time when a purpose-built ape enclosure was sitting empty and unused at the Wonderful World of Wildlife Zoo in east Kent. The move had been made with relative ease, and Natalie had been waiting to welcome them unaware of just what an impact this lowly immature female called Micha was about to have on her life.

Chapter 8
The Morning After

On the morning after Toby's first words with Micha, Natalie was delighted to see that he had made it their meeting place so quickly.

She knew he would be too keen to find out more for him to stay mad at her for long and it only made her more convinced that she had done the right thing by getting him to meet Micha the night before.

He had a breathless glow of excitement and nervous trepidation that was making him rock back and forwards, the desire to step back into the discovery of the night before battling with a fear of where it might take him — like all eleven-year-old boys, he wanted safety and danger in equal measure.

As much as the decision to bring Toby into their world had been tough on Natalie, it had been much tougher for Micha, who remained unconvinced. She knew enough of the human world by now to know that Toby was a young, boy equivalent in age to a chimpanzee of four or five years old and, as such, knew that the loss of his mother would be a terrible blow to him. She understood why Natalie wanted to help him, but also knew that many chimpanzees had suffered worse at the hands of humans and so was not as full of sympathy as Natalie was.

The two weeks from Alice's passing until the funeral had been a daily debate between Natalie and Micha T, with Natalie growing more confident with each round and Micha feeling more and more conflicted.

Eventually, it was Micha's yearning for more human conversation that had allowed her to be won over rather than any reasoned arguments from Natalie.

Micha sensed she had learned all that she could from the one-on-one sessions with her only human companion and she had been hungry, ravenous more like, for the chance to expand her world beyond the walls and bars of her enclosure.

Micha's one overriding wish was for her and her family to be free. She had decided over the two weeks of wrangling with Natalie that what she was actually being offered was a chance to befriend the son of the new owner of the zoo, the alpha male in her eyes, and if anyone could help her take her first step into freedom, it was him.

Natalie and Toby stood together at the locked gate at the back of the enclosure for a minute at the most until what seemed like a simultaneous strengthening of wills allowed them to push through the invisible barrier that was holding them back. Natalie had guided them in through the locked outer door into the rear holding pen. The concrete floors were wet from morning scrub down, and the air was chilled from a lack of morning sun and the cooling effect of the damp concrete under their feet. It was a lifeless shell of a building back then; it gave no hint of the vibrancy and animation that the chimpanzee world had in store for anyone who chose to journey further within.

As the door closed behind them, Natalie spoke first.

"I'm sorry we scared you last night, I didn't mean for that to happen. I wanted to give you something else to think about on such a horrible day, and I was so proud of how you had spoken that I didn't think about just how big a deal this was going to be for you."

"I'm sorry I ran off like that, I hope I didn't frighten Micha."

Natalie smiled at this; the thought that Micha being scared of any of the humans at the zoo, least of all the smallest one there.

Micha may only have been a metre tall on her hind legs, but she was as strong as two grown men and would grow stronger still by the time she reached full maturity in a year or two.

"Don't worry Toby, Micha is used to dealing with scary males, although I am not sure she has ever seen one run away from her before. My guess is that she would have got a real kick out of that." Natalie gave Toby a reassuring smile and guided him with a gentle arm over his shoulder towards the double-locked doors into the enclosure.

Natalie crossed the short corridor to the second, innermost door but did not attempt to open it. Instead, she stood there making a sharp, low hissing sound with her tongue against the back of her front teeth. Toby had guessed that this was her signal to Micha and was rewarded with his first sight of her moments later when she came over to the back of the enclosure and headed straight for the corner where Toby stood. Natalie passed back to join them as they huddled in the corner. They may have been no more than two feet apart, but they remained separated by the bars and wire mesh that marked the border between the chimpanzee world and the human one that lay outside.

"Morning, Micha. Look who's here. Toby has come back; you didn't frighten him away for good."

"Are you going to call me monkey again, No Hair?" Micha had stared deep into Toby's soul as she said those words, daring him to react, establishing a pecking order right from the start, making sure that she was not going to be on the bottom of this one.

"No, sorry about that, I know you are not a monkey. I was being rude. Yesterday was a very bad day, and I was tired. Sorry."

Micha, rocked back her head stretching her neck as she did, curling both lips out to show all her teeth and gave a high-pitched shriek that turned to very human sounding laughter, all the while clapping her hands and rocking from side to side.

"Don't be rude Micha. It's not polite to laugh at people, especially when they have said they are sorry. And don't call him No Hair, you know I don't like that phrase. His name is Toby Potter, and he wants to be a friend."

No Hair was a phrase that Micha used as a translation of the chimpanzee sound that alerted the troop to the news that a human was approaching. They differentiated themselves from humans in many ways, but most commonly it was by the lack of body hair, a physical characteristic that the chimpanzees found most ugly about humans.

Micha gradually ended her outburst of hilarity and gave a little shrug by way of an apology before putting her hand up to the mesh, palm open, waiting for Toby to follow suit. Encouraged by a nod from Natalie he inched a little closer and rested his palm flat against the wire so that their fingers could lock through the larger holes. His first touch of a chimpanzee sent an electric charge of excitement straight through Toby, and now it was his turn to laugh, a shrill peel that broke midway through into a deeper roll showing that he was at an age where his vocal cords were not something he had much control over.

For that brief but somehow eternal moment, Micha and Toby connected through the wire and the bars and across thousands of millennia of separation. Chimpanzees and humans, cousins of the animal kingdom, linked by a common ancestor and so alike in so many ways — aggressive, male-dominated, violent and oppressive but also loving, compassionate and intelligent. A small, grieving human boy on the cusp of adolescence and a maturing female chimpanzee with a gift that made her unique amongst all of the animals that have ever lived.

Micha spoke first to break the moment. "Why do humans have to be so ugly?"

"Micha!" Natalie's response took the form of a harsh rebuke. Micha shrugged another apology but softened her tone for her next words.

"Natalie told me about your Mum, I am sorry. She said you were very brave."

"Thank you. I don't want to talk about it." Toby dipped his head and kneeled to the ground beneath but kept his hand up, holding on to Micha's frightened to let it go, fearful of breaking their bond.

Micha held her gaze on Toby but with a depth of compassion in her eyes that transcended any barrier that stood between them. She softened her taught, squat, muscular frame and slowly lowered herself down to the floor, making her look almost submissive in her pose — the tears that had begun to flow across Toby's cheeks seemingly washing away any thoughts of dominance. A silence formed that threatened to engulf them both.

Toby looked up and smiled at Micha, using his free hand to quickly wipe away the tears.

"Do you like it here Micha?"

Micha let her hand drop from the mesh and folded it with her other in her lap, rocking back slightly to create a little distance between her and Toby.

"Do I like cold hard floors and metal bars?"

"Micha," Natalie let the tone in her voice translate what she was saying to her chimpanzee friend, "Be nice."

Micha rolled her eyes, a trademark expression of hers that conveyed her almost constant exasperation at humans and all of their precious feelings. She rocked forward again, a subtle shift in position that signalled a bridge being rebuilt between them.

"I am safe here. I am not hungry, and we have room to play outside, my troop is healthy, and no one threatens us."

Micha nodded as she spoke these words, but as she finished, she began to shake her head from side to side as if to disagree with what had just said. A pause hung in the air begging someone to end it.

"Do you like to play in the trees?" asked Toby with the simplicity of an eleven-year-old boy who still judged the success of a day out on how many trees were climbed, puddles jumped or streams dammed. Micha rolled her eyes again and this time locked her gaze on Natalie, a silent question carried in it, "Seriously? Is this who we broke our silence for?"

"Yes, I like to play in trees, but everywhere I climb there is always a bar or a fence stopping me going as far as I want to go. Outside is good but inside, in here." She swung her arm in an arc to show the extent of the concrete cell they spent each night in.

"Does this look like a jungle to you?" She slapped the cold, wet ground with both hands and rose to her feet like a spring beneath had been released. "This is not where chimpanzees live; this is not a forest floor."

Toby was startled by Micha's speed and the power she suddenly projected. He rushed his next question not thinking as he said it,

"What do you want us to do? How can we make it better?"

Natalie looked from Toby to Micha, excited by the question and eager to hear Micha's reply.

"There is only one thing you can do Toby; set me free. I want to go home. I want my feet to feel the jungle floor, and I want to climb trees that do not have bars around them. I want to see the jungle that my father and grandmother knew, the one where they were born. Take me home Toby, please. I want to be wild."

Both Natalie and Toby could sense that the conversation was over. Micha was standing with both arms holding the mesh and was rocking gently from side to side as if she was building the momentum to overcome the pull that was keeping her there.

As she watched the young chimpanzee start to leave Natalie knew with a sudden certainty that surprised even her what she had to do; she was going to take Micha, and as many of her family as possible back to the Congo jungle. She was going to take them home.

Chapter 9
Micha's Rules

Toby and Natalie left the enclosure as Micha loped across the empty hangar, heading for the outside arena.

Toby was stunned into an awed silence by what he had just witnessed and Natalie focusing on Micha's last words and how much they had meant to her.

Eventually, Toby broke the silence. "How have you kept this a secret for so long? And why?

"Because I love her, Toby, like she was my child and |I will do whatever I have to do to protect her. She is incredible Toby, the only animal in the world who can do what she does, and we have to protect her."

"Protect her from what? She is awesome. She will be the most famous ape in the world. Surely we have to tell Uncle Jack?"

"No, Toby! I've told you already" Natalie grabbed both his shoulders again, as she had done before but this time, she was much more firm in her grip.

"If we tell anyone, Jack included, we will never see her again, and she will never see her family again either. She wants to go back to the wild, and I agree with her. She is far too special to live out her days in a zoo, no matter how well we care for her here. We need to get her and her family back to the jungles of Central Africa where they belong."

Toby reacted in horror to what Natalie was suggesting. He had just met a talking ape, the only one in the world ever, and was being told that she was going to be taken away from him, sent back to a jungle? Not even sent back; she had never seen a jungle. Why would she want to go there where it was wild and dangerous, and you had to hunt and forage for your food? Why would anyone leave the luxury of a zoo for that?

Natalie was good at reading faces and could see much of what Toby was thinking as if he was miming it for her. She relaxed her grip on his shoulders and pulled him in close for a hug, remembering that he was a grieving child who was having to come to terms with not only the loss of his mum but also the shock of meeting a talking chimpanzee. When she released him from her embrace, she stayed crouched down, so she was eye to eye with him again.

"Toby, I know just how much this is for you to take in but I introduced you to Micha because I think you are an amazing young man and I think the two of you are going to be very important to each other. It will take years to relocate her and her family to Congo or the DRC and it may never happen, no matter how hard I try. You will get to spend a very long time together, and I know that you will learn a great deal from each other.

Here is what I think we should do."

And so it was that Natalie laid out her plan for Toby and Micha. She explained to him how he could meet with Micha at seven a.m. every morning for an hour before the keepers made their usual rounds of the ape arena and again in the evening for an hour at seven p.m. when she would be scheduled to do her final checks on the chimpanzees before closing them down for the night. When the three of them were together, they would be able to talk freely. At other times during the day if he wanted to come and sit by the enclosure or the arena, he could but if Micha did come over to him, she would not talk, even if Toby spoke to her. Micha was as keen as Natalie to maintain the secrecy regarding her incredible talent and was as fearful of her chimpanzee family finding out as she was of any more humans becoming aware.

Toby had relaxed a little at the news that he was going to have lots of time with Micha.

Natalie left Toby by the Polar Zone watching the penguins. She had spotted Jack coming in and did not want to be late for their morning meeting. Toby had promised her that he would go back to the cottage to let his dad know where he was, but it was Saturday morning, the sun was shining, and the zoo was his for another hour before the visitors were allowed in. Besides, all the guests from the night before would still be in the house and Toby did not want to talk to them right now, not when he could speak to Micha.

As soon as Natalie was out of sight, Toby left the penguins and headed back to the ape arena to see if he could spot Micha amongst the trees. The whole troop were out enjoying a climb and swing amongst the trees before their breakfast arrived. Toby could see Sundance sitting in his usual place high on the main branch in the far corner, a spot that gave him a full view over his domain. Butch and Sally were sat on a specially made wooden ledge halfway up the back wall and were grooming one another, deep in concentration. Kianza was swinging from rope to rope, on a circuit around the arena, followed as ever, by his twin shadows of Sonny and Fredo. Savannah was hunched over in the corner nearest the entrance with Cindy and Daphne carrying out their morning ritual of inspection for any tasty morsels that might be trapped in her hair, all the while making soft, reassuring hooting sounds as though they were singing to her.

Toby scanned the area searching for Micha and had expected to see her joining in with Kianza and the other two. It was just as he started to move from the glass wall at the front of the arena that Micha revealed herself. She had been watching him from a nearby treetop, masked by foliage; spying on him as if she had known all along that he would return so quickly.

She swung effortlessly to the ground, using both arms to rotate around the trunk of the tree using branches on either side to guide her decent. She dropped and rolled from the lowest one and landed inches from the glass wall just next to where Toby was standing. Toby instinctively put the palm of his hand up to the glass pane, but Micha responded with a bout of head shaking and nodding, vigorously shaking it to and fro, up and down, pausing briefly in between each movement to bare her teeth in a vast grin, half mocking, half joyful in its nature. Toby spoke to her through the glass.

"Micha, we need to talk. I have so much I want to say to you, and so much I want to learn."

Micha held his gaze but continued to swing her head from side to side, no longer smiling but frowning at him with a stern warning. Slowly she raised one outstretched finger to her lips and held it there long enough to make it clear that she was sending Toby a message, reminding him of his duty to protect her secret. She let the finger rest on her lip for a second or two more than was needed and then rocked her head back to release a single, shrieking peel of laughter and rolled over backwards before lopping off back to the trees to join Kianza on his rope swing.

Toby knew that there was no point in him hanging around any longer now as it was clear how Micha was going to be about the rules. He left the apes and started a slow stroll back home.

He took his time heading home, going the long way

round the zoo, desperate to delay getting back to the house and having to face any stark reminders of his mother's death. Despite his efforts, he was back in the cottage kitchen little more than an hour after leaving to meet Natalie. It felt like he had been gone a lifetime, though, the weight of his responsibility to Natalie and Micha pressing on him hard but making him stronger in the process.

He was pleased to hear that the cottage was silent and assumed his dad had gone to the main house to be with the other guests but as he entered the lounge, he saw that he was not alone. He could see his dad sat motionless in his chair beside the corner desk, staring into the unlit fire. Dan looked up to greet Toby; his face etched with deep lines from where his head had been in his hands, the lines like those on a street map, every road leading to despair. His eyes were red and empty looking, so many tears had flowed that no more could follow. He started to speak, but no words could leave his lips, no smile could form; as if the lips refused to lie, to say "we are happy, everything is OK". He merely shook his head and put his arms out, in mute appeal, desperate for comfort but too raw and too sad to ask for it.

The moment Toby saw his dad like this he was stabbed with a dagger of guilt, his stomach forcing its way into his chest, pushing his heart into his throat. He rushed to his dad and buried his head in his shoulder whispering again and again.

"I'm sorry Dad, I'm sorry, I shouldn't have left you, I'm sorry."

Dan could not reply, too ashamed that it was his son who was doing the comforting and not him. He squeezed Toby in as close as he could, trying to join them as one, making sure they could never be separated again.

His dad had been a faint outline of his former self at the funeral yesterday, and Toby knew that it was going to take months or years to try and fill him back in. He sat, awkwardly at first, in his dad's lap, arm over his shoulder and rested against him, forehead to forehead. They stayed like that for ten minutes or more, as if their touching heads were allowing shared thoughts and feelings to pass, unspoken, between them.

Finally, Toby spoke, "Dad can we stay in the cottage; I don't want to move back into the main house, it's too big for…" He was going to say, "for the two of us", but he wasn't able to say that yet, too frightened that the words would make it real, confirm to him that his mum was gone and he would never see her again.

Dan had heard the unfinished part of the sentence and nodded to let Toby know that he couldn't say it either.

"Sure son, of course, we can. We have everything we need 'ere; we can turn the main house into offices or an 'otel or something, we don't need all them rooms."

The act of making a decision seemed to spur them both on and allowed them to move through to the main house. Toby knew that the rest of the day would be spent in the company of friends and family and suddenly that seemed like the perfect thing to do.

Deep down though he knew the most important meeting of the day would be at seven p.m. when he could go back to the ape arena.

Chapter 10
Natalie Goes to Work on Jack

After leaving Toby by the penguins, Natalie had gone straight to catch up with Jack who was heading for the main office hut.

The office was on the edge of the zoo, in a wooded part of the park, next to the other administration buildings which included the one Natalie had been living in for the past five years.

Natalie had grown very fond of Dr Jack Friday MRCVS, MSc, PhD over the past few months. Jack had been working part time at the zoo for a couple of years before the Potters took over and was now there almost as much as Natalie. She looked forward to their morning meetings with a level of excitement that she was struggling to believe was purely work-related. Natalie was twenty-eight years old and had been single for almost her entire twenties. She was not sure, but she guessed that Jack was at least ten years older and knew that he was every bit as single as she was. In her darker moments, Natalie had a vision of herself in her fifties, alone and still living in a converted Portacabin, a mad cat woman whose cats were the type that could kill you and eat you for breakfast and be hungry by dinnertime. At times she was comfortable with this vision. She loved her work and didn't care much where she lived so long as it was as close to her beloved animals as possible and unless she moved into one of the enclosures, she could not get any closer than where she lived now. But there were other times, usually, late night after a glass of wine, that she had to admit that she did, sometimes, want the company of another human and working with Jack every day was making these feelings come a little more frequently and didn't even need a glass of wine to prompt them.

Jack looked forward to these meetings every bit as much as Natalie and, like her, had chosen to keep this a secret.

Jack was smitten with Natalie.

He had been from the moment he first saw that shock of electric blue hair exploding above her tanned, athletic frame. She had an easy, confident smile and caring, forgiving brown eyes that bathed Jack in her full attention whenever they spoke. Unfortunately for a man who could rugby tackle a rhino, Jack was literally petrified, frozen to the point of complete immobility when it came to speaking to any woman he was attracted to. He could manage professional conversations, of course. He could talk about the various dietary needs of a dozen different species of Lemur or list every variation in the Siberian tiger's nerve supply to its hind legs but when faced with the opportunity to tell a woman that he liked her, his body turned to marble, and his brain turned to mush. It was no surprise, then, that romance between the two of them had been moving at a pace somewhere between glacial and tectonic.

But in the meeting on that particular day, Natalie was not in the least bit distracted by any thoughts of a romantic nature; she was totally focused on her plan to relocate Micha and Micha's family to the Congo jungle. She had arrived at the hut no more than two minutes behind Jack, but he had already poured and nearly finished his first coffee of the day. He had the cup to his lips as she walked in.

"We need to think about a relocation program for Sundance and his family. The troop is too large, and in a year or two, Kianza will be a threat, sooner maybe if he can get Sonny and Fredo to back him against his father. Who do we still know working on the ground in DCR?"

Jack lowered his cup and smiled.

"Morning Natalie, how are you?"

"Sorry, sorry Jack. It's just that I have come from the ape arena and I was watching the younger males. Their play is getting more aggressive, and Sundance is going to have to do something soon to protect his status; I am worried that it might get out of hand. I used to work in the Bili-Uele region close to the northern border of the DRC, I think I might still have some contacts who can help us with a relocation, how about you? Isn't your friend Frank still down that way? If we start now, they could be there by the end of the year; we can go with them, you and me and the chimpanzees. We can stay in my old lodges there. What do you think?"

Natalie was talking at least double her normal speed, and the words were getting out far quicker than her mouth could check to see if they made any sense or not. Jack looked at her with a face of pure wonder. He loved her. He loved her energy, her intelligence, her optimism, her passion, her hair, her smell. He loved the speed she walked around the park, her broad, muscular shoulders, her face wide grin, the way she put her head to one side when she asked a question, the way she subconsciously signed everything she was saying when she got excited and the way she held him in gaze that he never wanted to finish. He was powerless to resist her.

"You're right, we do need to move them, but six months is completely unrealistic. We can try to talk to the chimpanzee trust in Kisangani, Frank is the director there but he's always out in the field. This could take two years easily; the paperwork alone will take six months just to get approval for the plan. We may have to move the younger males and maybe Micha before then, for their safety."

"No! We can't move Micha. We mustn't!"

Natalie couldn't help herself; the shriek was out of her mouth before her hands could catch it.

She had somehow made herself taller than she already was and had puffed up in a protective stance, chin out and chest up just as any other ape would have done if they felt their offspring being threatened. Jack took a step back instinctively, spilling his coffee as he did; the cup failing to keep up with where his lips were going.

"Steady there, Nats. I know you are fond of Micha, but you and I know she is going to be fully mature soon and if she stays in that troop the young males are not going to be able to control themselves. Things will get messy, and Sundance isn't exactly renowned for his diplomatic skills."

Natalie knew that Jack was right, but she spent the rest of the meeting trying to gently persuade him that he was wrong. She explained how they needed to focus on the Congo, and not other zoos dotted around the UK and Europe. She stressed just how much Sundance had suffered at the hands of humans already and how he and Savannah had enough memory of life in the wild to make the transition safe for the whole family.

Jack certainly had warmed to the idea. Partly because he would have agreed to set his trousers on fire if Natalie had asked him to but also because he knew about Sundance's terrible history. Jack was certain that he did not want to be the next in a long line of humans to abuse and mistreat such an incredible animal.

Only once she felt certain that she had Jack on board with her plan did Natalie allow the meeting to move on and when she did, she remembered that Jack was Alice's brother and yesterday he had had to bury his sister. She felt dreadful for not saying anything at the start of the meeting and felt even worse trying to say something without making it obvious that she had forgotten. In the end, she just got up mid-sentence from her chair and hugged him.

It was a long silent embrace that felt just right to her, but left Jack bewildered and trying to answer the fifty different questions that had just stormed into his brain. It was five seconds at least before he realised that he hadn't actually joined in the hug and was simply standing there like some rolled up carpet that Natalie was trying to pick up. Slowly, tentatively Jack put his arms around Natalie and buried his head next to hers. They stood like this for somewhere between two minutes, and a lifetime, Jack wasn't entirely sure: but when they broke apart, he looked at her and said,

"Thank you; I didn't realise how much I needed that. I don't think I've hugged anyone properly since Alice di..." the word stuck in his throat. He realised why she had done it and he loved her even more; he had to turn away quickly as he could feel tears forming and knew he would not be able to stop them if they did.

By the end of the meeting that day neither was any

the wiser as to how they felt about each other but they were, at least, united in a desire to take Sundance and his family home.

Chapter 11
How the Inmates See the Guards

From when he had left Natalie that morning, Toby had spent the rest of his day talking with relatives and eating an assortment of leftovers that could have fed all the visitors to the zoo for a week.

He and his dad had been inseparable all day, the sum of their strengths seemingly far greater than that of their two parts. By the time that late afternoon was prepared to admit that it was actually early evening the guests took an invisible cue that said it was time to leave.

Dan and Toby stood on the steps of the main house and waved them off. They stood there, alone together for a last minute's silence, hushed in exhausted remembrance of their beloved wife and mother, hands held and heads bowed. Their silence was suddenly broken by the sound of a lion's roar, Achilles letting the world know that he was awake and hungry. Dan and Toby looked at each other, both unable to hold back a smile at the perfect way to end their spontaneous, silent memorial.

"I'm too tired to face the house, Toby; I'm going

back to the cottage. Want to watch a film with me?"

On any other day of his life, Toby would have jumped at the chance to sit and watch a film with his dad. No matter how guilty it made him feel, though, he knew he was going to have to say no to his dad as he had a meeting that he could not and would not miss. He told his dad that he was meeting Natalie as she had offered to let him help with the chimpanzee last feed which his dad knew was a favourite zoo activity. Dan smiled again at Toby, so proud of how strong his boy was and happy at how well he had adjusted to zoo life after leaving London. He rubbed Toby's head and let his hand trail down the side of his face, cupping his son's cheek in his palm and patting him gently before waving him off.

Toby arrived early hoping to steal a little one on one time with Micha. Natalie, of course, was way ahead of him, knowing just what Toby might try.

"I said seven p.m. kiddo, and no talking to Micha without me present. You know the rules Toby. I didn't keep all this secret for the past five years to have you blow it the day after I bring you in."

Toby knew he was busted and made a note not to test Natalie on this in the future. No matter what, he was just happy to be there and to know that he was about to talk to Micha again.

When they walked into the enclosure, Natalie and Toby could see Micha was sat in the corner by the doorway t but she was not alone. She was joined by Kianza and they appeared to be deep in conversation, heads touching brow to brow with low, resonant hoots and short, sharp barks passing between them in what seemed to be the starting of a bitter row. As soon as Micha spotted the two humans entering the enclosure, however, she pushed herself back from Kianza ending their conversation with a pursed lip "hssssh" sound making them look like two startled school kids surprised by the sudden presence of a teacher in the classroom. She rose up on to her feet and using her knuckles for support bounded across the concrete floor to greet her friends, crabbing sideways with her body angled forty-five degrees to the direction she was heading.

She looked excited to see them both and shook her head wildly from side to side before coming to a halt when she reached the fence, deep in the corner nearest the double locked entrance. Micha must have stored a little parcel of food there ready for the meeting as she dug out a handful of chopped mango and apple along with a ball of the mashed vegetable cake that was known to the zookeepers as 'monkey chow." Natalie had made sure that as much as possible the apes were not fed directly but instead tried to ensure that the food was distributed around the enclosure and the

arena so that all the chimpanzees had to spend at least part of their day foraging for food as they would have done in the wild. She also made sure that no one referred to the cake as 'monkey chow' in front of Micha, knowing she would never hear the end of it if the young chimpanzee got wind of what they called it.

Micha settled into the corner, sitting down with her back to the fence so she could face Toby and Natalie. She pulled a strip of mango flesh from the lump in her hand and began to chew on it methodically as she focused her gaze on Toby who was sat opposite her, less than two feet away separated by a thin wire mesh only. Toby took the time to take in the view of Micha as she stared at him. Her young eyes wide open but deep set beneath her prominent brow, contrasting with her wrinkled skin all around the sockets that gave her the appearance of youthful innocence and aged wisdom all at the same time. Her black hair surrounded her pinkish brown face and sprouted at wild and divergent angles around her ears giving her a look of someone trapped in a permanent 'bad hair' day. She had a distinctive white streak that emphasised her centre parting and added to her look of being older than her years.

"What were you and Kianza arguing about?" asked Toby, eager to begin the evening's chat.

A tiny but perceptible change took hold of Micha's expression. She had been spending too much time with Natalie over the past few years, and she had picked up some of her human characteristics. The change lasted the briefest of moments, but Toby spotted it and saw it for what it was; a mixture of guilt and surprise. She had indeed been arguing with Kianza and was not proud of what had been said, but she had not expected a human to know this, least of all Toby who she had only met yesterday.

"Were you talking about us?" Toby continued, pointing at Natalie and him as he spoke.

Toby was soon to turn twelve years old, but he had not lost that sense that all young children have that allows them to read faces so well, alert to the slightest changes in the moods of those they rely on most. He drew in close to Micha, suddenly aware that there was something important to be said.

Natalie stood back from Micha and Toby as if her role was that of an old-fashioned chaperone, her presence there a requirement to ensure correct decorum but not to join in the proceedings. Micha reinforced this impression by shooting her a glance that said, "Give us a moment, would you?" A simple shift of her eyes and furrowing of her brow was all that was needed to give

Natalie the feeling that Micha wanted some privacy with Toby. It was a bizarre and uncomfortable feeling for her to take. Natalie had been the centre of Micha's universe for almost five years, and in one sideways glance, she suddenly felt that the stars and the planets had shifted slightly to make room for a new sun for Micha to revolve around.

Micha bent her head forward and spoke low, the words intended for Toby's ears only.

"Yes, we were talking about you and yes we were arguing. Kianza was telling me that I must not spend time with you No Hairs any more. He thinks you will try and steal me or kill me for food. He has been speaking with Sundance, and this is what he thinks all humans do. I told Kianza he was wrong and that he was stupid; he did not take it well. He thinks we should kill you first before you kill us."

Chapter 12
The News for Toby gets Worse

Toby stared in disbelief at Micha, silently, desperately searching for the first word that might make some sense of the situation.

He clasped the wire mesh and pushed his forehead against the fence as if his physical presence would somehow make up for the lack of speech. Finally, the words came to him.

"Kill you? Are you mad Micha? You are the most precious thing we have. Natalie loves you. She spends her whole day making sure you are safe and well looked after. She would never harm you and neither would I. We love you."

"She killed Ursula, the brown bear, yesterday — we heard about that this morning."

Toby made an involuntary twist of his head towards Natalie, shooting her an accusative look as he did but Micha grabbed his hand through the fence, urging him to stop before Natalie got wind of the conversation.

"Don't let on what we are talking about. Natalie mustn't know that I know about Ursula."

"Why not?" asked Toby, uncertain at first as to why

it would matter if Natalie knew or not.

As his words filled the space between the two of them a realisation dawned on him — how could Micha know about Ursula if Natalie hadn't told her. Micha had said that she found out this morning, but Toby had been there with them this morning and nothing was said, Natalie hadn't even mentioned it to Toby before or after the chat with Micha. He had heard that Ursula had been unwell, and Jack was worried about her, but that was as much as he knew.

Toby locked his questioning gaze on Micha and was met with a sorrowful look in return. They stared at each other through the fence. Toby lifted his other hand to the mesh and felt Micha squeeze hers around his so that they had both hands clasped together.

Micha moved her head in as well so that their foreheads touched through the gaps in the mesh. As they held this pose Toby was whispering to Micha, almost chanting, "We won't hurt you Micha, we love you. We will keep you safe; no one will hurt you."

Just as Toby was beginning to believe in the strength of his words Kianza tore into the picture, crashing through the invisible wall they had built around them.

He had been crouched quietly at the far side of the enclosure by the entrance to the arena. Micha had made the mistake of thinking that he would get bored and head outside for a last forage as he usually did around this time. But Kianza had decided to stick around, partly because of what he and Micha had been talking about but mainly because of how their argument had ended. He had been unable to convince Micha of the threat the No Hairs represented and was unnerved by how close Micha had become to them. He had accepted Micha's reassurances when there was the female human only, but now that a male had turned up, even if he was an immature, weak looking one, Kianza could no longer stand back and allow this threat to his position go unchallenged.

The attack by Kianza was as brief as it was terrifying. Kianza had launched himself from sitting to full height, with arms extended to make himself look as tall as possible. He had run at the fence where Toby was sat, covering the ground in two or three seconds, his mouth open wide, lips back and all teeth bared with murderous intent. The peace in the enclosure was shattered by a terrible, "Aakaak" sound that Kianza was barking out again and again. He lashed violently at Micha, an open-handed blow landing on the back of her head and sending her cowering into the corner crying out in shrieks of pain.

In his attempt to get at Toby, Kianza stamped on Micha's exposed back as he flung both arms against the partition, crashing his fists against the mesh in the area where Toby's head had gently rested moments before. He grabbed hold of the fence long enough to allow him to bring his feet onto it as well so he could use all four limbs to shake the wire mesh as violently as possible. His cries reached a crescendo of rage as saliva sprayed from his open mouth, a white-hot glare burning in his eyes.

Toby had pushed himself away from the fence with his feet, sliding across the wet concrete floor but had come to rest no more than a leg's length away from this explosive rampage. Kianza's saliva sprayed on to his chest and face before he had a chance to rise to his feet and rush to the gate and outstretched arms of Natalie. By the time he reached Natalie the attack was over. Kianza had made his point and established full dominance over the puny No Hair. He let go of the fence and loped off to the arena in a low, sideways run using his knuckles for support looking back briefly to check that Micha had got the message as well. For her part, Micha was hunched down in the corner furthest from where she had been sitting moments before, face down with arms wrapped protectively over her head ready to fend off any further blows. Kianza changed his call to a deep but still threatening hoot that made Micha nod furiously as she mimicked the call, in reply.

Natalie knew that Toby was safe from the attack but had reached instinctively for the cleaning hose that was used to spray cold water on any such an assault if a human was inside the enclosure. She realised afterwards that she had done this to protect Micha, treating her as a human and not an ape. Toby was suddenly shocked and almost ashamed to find that he had hugged Natalie around her waist and was standing, half hid behind her. He quickly released his grasp and stepped back in front of her and rushed down the corridor to the site of the attack to check that Micha was okay.

"Micha, are you all right? Are you hurt?" Micha looked up and let Toby know that she was all right with a gentle shake of her head to the last question and what seemed to all the world like a knowing wink. She took a quick glance around the area to confirm that she was alone before letting the briefest of smiles crack across her lips. She rolled forward onto her knuckles and crawled across the floor to join Toby somehow managing to make her efforts seem more like a saunter than a crawl. By the time she had reached Toby she had regained her full composure and was keen to let him know that she had had the situation under control the whole time. She finished the last few steps to the mesh upright with her arms up again managing to pull off a hint of swagger as she reached the fence and placed her palms against it.

"Sorry about Kianza, he can play at bit rough sometimes," she said, her tone clearly intended to lighten the mood and calm Toby's nerves. Natalie had stayed back at the gate, keeping an eye out for any keepers who might have heard the commotion. She did not seem too concerned by what had just happened, so

Toby felt relaxed enough to let out a speculative laugh, not able to hide entirely the uncertainty and caution held within it.

"What was that all about?" he asked, "Why was he so angry with me?"

"You are a male, so he feels he has to show you he is the boss. When it was just Natalie, he didn't feel threatened as she is female."

"Nothing to do with thinking that I might try to kill you then."

"Well, that too," Micha shrugged a little as she said this and sat back down, "He is going to take some convincing about that."

"You believe me though don't you Micha?"

Toby could not hide the desperate plea in his voice as he asked this. He could not believe that Micha would think this of him or Natalie and it was essential to him that he convinced her otherwise.

"I like you Toby, and I believe that you do not want to kill me, but you just promised me that you would protect me and not let anyone hurt me and that just happened." She pointed to the exit to the arena as she finished her sentence emphasising the extent of the threat she was under from the rest of her kind. "You can't keep me safe in here Toby. This is my world but the more time I spend with you and Natalie the less I feel like I belong here and the more at risk I will become from Kianza and all the other males. I am still young enough to get some protection from the other females, but this won't last for long. I don't want to be in the troop any more. I need to get out of here Toby; I need to be free."

Toby realised she was right. He could not protect her here in the enclosure from her species or outside it from his. He was nodding his agreement but could not shake a question that he had been about to ask her before Kianza attacked.

"How did you know about Ursula? Even I didn't know about that."

Micha looked down to the ground and began to sway like she did when she was about to pull away from the conversation, as she had done last night but this time she stayed, raising her head to meet Toby's gaze once more. She puffed up her cheeks as if she was holding back the words in her mouth, frightened to let them out. The truth was that she was desperate to confide in Toby, bursting to tell someone about the secret she had held back from Natalie this whole time.

Micha examined Toby's face looking for a final clue to make it clear to her whether she should tell him or not. In the end, though she could find no confirmation, perhaps just a level of innocence and trust that finally let the words escape from her tightly sealed lips.

"The green birds told me, the ones you call parrots; they tell me everything."

And so it was that Micha went on to explain how she knew about Ursula, how all the animals around the zoo knew; they had talked about it.

The truth about animals is that nearly all of them can communicate with each other. Maybe not as much as Micha and Natalie could do but certainly enough to share necessary information and pass a message along, species to species, perhaps when a common enemy threatened, or water had been found in a dry spell. It was a skill learned in the wild over countless generations of evolution. In zoos, it was taught by any wild born animals to any of those born in captivity.

In the zoo, the chief news broadcasters were Del Boy and Rodney. They were the eyes and ears of the zoo and could be trusted to spread news and gossip around the park quicker than the sound waves carrying it.

The news of Ursula had been shocking for all to hear.

All of the animals liked and trusted Natalie. She showed them all so much affection and such respect that any suggestion of her killing one of them was tough to take.

Del Boy and Rodney had been spreading the news for several days that Ursula was sick and had a pain in her stomach and could not eat her food. They had let it be known that for the last three days she had not been able to stand and was crying out to the other bears to help her. They told how Natalie had gone into Ursula's rocky cave enclosure with a stranger and when they had come out a few minutes later Ursula was dead; a few hours later a truck had come and taken her body away.

Toby sat in amazed silence, scarcely able to take in the enormity of what he was experiencing. A talking Ape was explaining to him how almost every animal on earth can talk to each other and mostly what they were saying was "Beware! Humans are the enemy."

He glanced over to Natalie a couple of times, little more than nervous twitches to check that she was still there, but Micha squeezed his hand each time to make him keep his focus on her. She told him that Natalie did not know about the common language and explained that she had kept it from her to help protect all the other animals. Micha was worried that if Micha told her, then she would want to know all about the language and would use it to control them even more. As ever Toby was quick to defend Natalie.

"You're wrong Micha, Natalie would never do that. You must understand, Ursula was very sick, she was in a lot of pain. There was nothing Uncle Jack could do to save her. If Natalie had put her to sleep then there must have been a reason; she would have suffered terribly for many more hours or days. It was the kindest thing to do, I promise you. All she wants to do is protect you all."

"Protect us? Who from? In the wild, we chimpanzees can fight off a leopard, who do you think we need protecting from? Who is Sobek the crocodile so frightened of that he needs to hide in a little pond? Who is Achilles the lion so threatened by that he needs to be kept locked up in a cage?"

Toby was shocked by the question. He had not thought about it before, why did all these animals need protection? Who were they protecting them from? Then it dawned on him, and the answer made him ashamed.

"It's us Micha. We are protecting you from us. Humans are the enemy."

Chapter 13
The Truth About Zoos

Toby did not stay to talk with Micha for much longer that evening.

The pain of realisation that he was both her prison guard and her biggest threat was too much for him to take. He had suddenly wanted to speak with his own kind; he needed to talk to Natalie and Jack about the animals, unable to handle so many conflicting thoughts on his own.

They spoke a few more words to each other and Micha still held his hand even after what he had said. She knew that Toby was right about humankind being the enemy, but she also knew that the young, frightened, grieving little boy sat in front of her was not a threat; he was a friend to be trusted. Micha was also aware who Toby was and what rank he held in the human troop.

Like all young female chimpanzees, Micha had had to learn almost from birth that she could not get her way by the strength of her threatening displays like the males did; she had to use her cunning to get others to help her with her plans. Micha had become an expert at this. If she wanted Sundance to give up a particularly tasty looking morsel of food or relinquish a prime perch, then it was Kianza who would do the work for her. A subtle suggestion or a carefully executed ruse to trick him and his twin shadows of Fredo and Sonny would set a chain of events in motion that could be assured to get Micha her prize with none of the males aware of what part they had played in it all. Micha had seen in Toby not just a friend but also a potential ally to get her out from behind these bars and glass walls; to set her free. She needed him, and she knew it.

Once Micha had left, Toby stood and faced Natalie; a thousand questions jostling for a place in the queue forming at the back of his throat. She could see he was troubled but assumed it was the attack by Kianza that had been the problem. As they locked the gate behind them and made their way into the dying warmth of the June evening, Toby started to dig.

"How is Ursula doing? Uncle Jack was worried about her."

"Oh Toby, I didn't want to tell you after everything else that has happened. We had to put her to sleep she had bowel cancer, and there was nothing else we could have done. I had to call in another vet; I couldn't make your uncle deal with that as well, not with the funeral yesterday."

Toby stayed silent as he took this on board. He had known that Natalie would have been doing what was best for Ursula. He had grown to trust her implicitly when it came to the animals at the zoo; her love for them all was evident to see. But something was troubling him now, Micha had made him question her actions. It made him think of his mum. The wound that the loss of his mother had left in him was still so raw and open that is almost made it too painful for him to examine the similarities between her last breaths in the hospital bed and Ursula's spent alone and frightened on a concrete floor. Did she wish her family were with her, holding her tight? Would it have been better for her in the wild, alone in the Alaskan forest with no one to hear her cries? He was so confused.

When they had first arrived at the zoo, it was only the second time in his life he had been to one. The first had been on a school trip to London Zoo in Regent's Park when he had only really cared about going to the snake house like his namesake Harry did in *The Philosopher's Stone*. He had never questioned why we have zoos or if they were good or bad. He had just assumed that they always existed and that the animals liked it there. It was a comfortable assumption, and he had never bothered to explore it further, trusting as most young children do, that adults know best.

But Micha had pulled him out from under that comfort blanket and made him face the truth no matter how uncomfortable it made him feel. She had made him see that animals had feelings just like he did. He was suddenly aware that his dad owned a zoo that had hundreds of animals in and maybe none of them wanted to be there. Was he part of some evil plan to keep animals as prisoners or slaves against their will? Should he sneak out at night and set them all free?

He nodded to Natalie to show that he had heard her and that he understood what she had said, but he wanted to know more.

"Was she frightened when you came to her with the vet?"

"No, of course not Toby, she didn't know what we were going to do. She was in pain; all she would have wanted was to be out of pain."

"What about Mum? Would you have done the same to her when she was in pain?" Toby suddenly felt a sense of heat and anger to his pain that was making him spit the words out, aggressive stabbing questions trying to wound more than enquire, bitter tears welling, uninvited as he spoke.

"No Toby! Of course not. We all loved your mum, we all wanted her to get well. We would never have done anything like that to her."

"Why Ursula then? Why is she different?"

"Toby?" his name used as a question and a sigh of exasperation. "Ursula is an animal. We can't ask her what she wants. She doesn't think like us. Bears have simple lives; they raise young and let them go their own way — they eat all summer so they can sleep most of the winter. She was old for a bear, and it was her time.

To do nothing would have been the cruellest thing of all. You must see that."

They made it back to the cottage before Toby was able to find an answer to her question. He said goodbye to Natalie and promised her he would be at the Enclosure at seven a.m. tomorrow and no earlier. He went inside and was overjoyed to see his Uncle Jack in the kitchen, kettle in hand making himself a coffee. Jack turned to see Toby enter the room and had only just enough time to put the pot down before Toby was on top of him wrapping his arms around him and burying his head deep into his chest.

"Whoa there, Toby Dick, what's up Little Big Man?"

Toby couldn't speak at first, fearful that his voice would betray him, or the tears would return, but after listening to reassuring sounds of Jack's chest, he was able to mumble.

"We need to talk."

He pulled himself away so he could sit at the breakfast bar and wait for Jack to take the cue and join him. Jack never liked to be too far from his nearest caffeine hit so finished making his coffee before he sat down opposite Toby.

"Why do we keep all these animals in cages? It's cruel, we should set them all free."

Jack had not been expecting this from Toby, having assumed he would want to talk about his mum.

"I know it seems cruel Toby, but without this zoo, these animals might not survive. Most of them have been rescued from the wild, and the rest were born in zoos, they would not know how to survive if we put them back."

"But they only needed to be rescued from us; we destroyed their world then we put them in cages. We keep them alive for a while, and then when they get sick, we put them to sleep."

The last phrase was spat out like a bad taste, contempt dripping from each syllable.

"That's a bit harsh my friend; I like to think I do a bit more than that. Natalie and I make sure all of the animals are kept in the best possible shape, we try to give them things to do every day to make their lives more interesting, trying to keep things as natural as possible and we do everything we can to help them when they get sick. I operated on three animals last week alone; you know how hard we worked to save that yellow headed Amazon parrot, Goliath.

He had an obstructed bowel, and it took me hours to fix him — he's fine now and probably out looking for the next bit of litter he can jam his gut up with."

Jack had been stung by Toby's accusation, and the hurt showed in his face.

"Mate, you know my view on mankind — we are the biggest natural disaster to hit this planet. We are acting like a spaceman smoking in his helmet and using his suit as a toilet. If we are not killing every animal we can for fun, we are choking them with plastic or burning down their habitat so I can have cheaper coffee. The three biggest large land animal populations on the planet are cows, pigs and sheep and the commonest bird is the chicken. Ninety-five per cent of all large land animals alive when we evolved are now extinct, because of us.

We won't stop until nothing is left but us and our food, and we'll keep them in cages because there will be no grass left either."

Jack had stood up and was pacing the kitchen floor, gathering speed as his rant began to build. But he looked at Toby and could see that he had already said too much.

He stopped pacing and went to sit beside his nephew, squeezing him tight to his chest.

"I know it's not perfect what we do here at the park but it's the best that we've got. We can't change the world Toby, and I'm not even sure we can save it, but I know we can save parts of it. If I have to choose between there being no golden tailed tamarins in the world or there being half a dozen left alive here in this zoo, then I know which I'm going to take. We are the last refuge for those little ginger beauties, and I will fight for them with all my considerable strength." He lifted Toby out of his chair and hugged him as he said this, "and I am going to make sure they survive for as long as I do, and a lot longer if possible."

Toby loved it when his uncle picked him up like

that. There was no effort in the lift, Jack's huge arms carried him like his hands were empty. Toby adored his uncle and felt comforted by his words and his presence, but he still wanted to push further, driven by a need to stand up for Micha.

"What about the chimpanzees though? Couldn't we set them free? There is still plenty of jungle left in Congo isn't there? That's where they come from right?" Toby had tried to affect a slightly disinterested tone to these questions as if they were little more than a passing thought — he didn't pull it off. Jack laughed as a dawning realisation hit him.

"Who's been talking to Natalie then?" His smile showed Toby that Jack was on to him and that he was happy about the conspiring that had been going on.

"I don't blame you, Toby. Natalie is an incredible woman and the only person here that cares more about these animals than I do. Nats spoke to me this morning about Sundance and his troop. She is right, it is getting too big, and too many of the males are going to mature at the same time.

Kianza is a beast; you do not want to be near him when he kicks off. He will be able to take on Sundance in a year, and it is going to turn messy when that happens. I agree with her, we need to relocate some of them, but I'm not sure where to. No other UK zoo can take them, certainly not more than one or two anyway. We may have to split them up, Micha will be no problem, lots of zoos are looking for females to breed with."

It was like Jack had poked Toby with a sharp stick, he yelped at the mention of Micha and shocked Jack just like Natalie had done that morning.

"Blimey, what is it with you and Nats when I talk about Micha? She's the obvious one to move first."

"No, we can't move her to another zoo, she needs to be with her family. We need to move them back to the Congo; she needs to be free."

"You and Natalie have been talking, haven't you? Have you guys packed your jungle bags already? I agree the Congo is the right place for them and if it could happen in time then great, but it isn't realistic, not in the time frame that we've got. It could take a couple of years to organise a relocation program back to Africa and in the area that we need to get to, the situation on the ground can change in a week. We have to do what's best for all the chimpanzees. We can't risk having one of them injured, or maybe even killed once Kianza, and Sonny and Fredo start throwing their weight around for real. We need to take some of them out before then, and it is easier to move them separately than as half the troop. Sorry Toby, I know that's not what you wanted to hear."

Toby sat in silence for a minute after Jack had spoken. It might have looked like he was sulking, a spoiled kid angry at not getting his own way, but that was not the case. Toby was concentrating, keeping still so as not to disturb the plan that was just starting to make itself felt in the corner of his mind.

Chapter 14
Sundance Says Hello

There is an area in the northern regions of Congo, close to the border between the Central African Republic and the Democratic Republic of Congo that is known as the Bili-Uele Forest. It is the size of Ireland and remains largely unexplored.

This vast expanse of untouched rainforest is home to what may be the last 'mega-culture' of chimpanzees on the planet. It is so far from normal human civilisation that it has been left untouched for centuries and this has allowed the chimpanzees to develop into a vast, common population, numbered in the thousands. The apes show shared customs and tools and worked together to defend their enormous territory, using unusually large males to patrol the perimeter where they ward off attacks from potential predators.

Toby knew this because he had left Jack in the kitchen that night, and gone to his room, fired up his laptop and spent half the night reading about the Congo Jungle.

He was in awe of the mighty Congo River, all two thousand and seven hundred miles of it. This colossal wall of water that has run through the heart of Africa for almost two million years. Rising from the mountains of the East Africa Rift it carves through the dense jungle, feeding and nurturing the mighty forests and its incredible inhabitants until it reaches the shores of the Atlantic Ocean. As he read about it Toby began to think of the Congo River as being the lifeblood of the planet. It had formed the land that humans had evolved from like it was the birth canal of our species; as if Mother Nature herself had bathed in its waters.

Toby had read about this unimaginable land until nearly two a.m., falling asleep to the hum of insects and the night calls of the wild.

By the time he woke a few hours later, he was clear in his mind what he needed to do and was waiting by the rear entrance to the enclosure at 6.59 a.m. with an atlas in his hand, ready to hit Natalie with his plan the second she arrived.

He had chatted to Jack in the past about Sundance, asking where he had come from and from what they could tell from his records he had been found in a village near to Bondo which is a town on the river Uele, the same river that gives its name to the Bili-Uele Forest. As soon as Toby had read about the mega-culture of chimpanzees of this region and their unusually large and aggressive males who patrol the area, he knew he had found where Sundance had come from and where he needed to get him and his family back to. Toby's recent loss had given him a sense of connection with Sundance and made him feel somehow responsible for all that had happened to him. He was desperate to make it up to him.

Even though it was Monday morning and there were still two weeks of school term left, Toby was not going in today. Since the death of his mum a fortnight ago school had not happened. With only ten days until the end of the year, Dan had decided he could miss the rest of the term and Toby had not argued the point. Toby had felt that his childhood had ended two weeks ago and the thought of going back to a primary school where mums stood by the gates, arms outstretched waiting to scoop up their excited little ones as they ran to them was too much. He couldn't bear the idea of the silent stares and the well-meaning questions from his friends — the sympathetic gazes and words of comfort from the teachers. His grief made him unable to step back into that world of friends who had known him when he had a mum. He refused to stay bound to that previous life where a mum will pick you up from a party or take you swimming or make you tea when your friends have come home from school with you.

He had checked in on his dad before heading out to meet Natalie. Toby had taken it upon himself to act as a buffer between his dad and the outside world. He was going to care for him and protect him for the worst of the insult and injury that Alice's death had caused him. This sense of purpose gave Toby strength and was helping him cope with his misery and bitter incomprehension of all that had happened.

"What's with the atlas?" asked Natalie as she strode up the path to the enclosure rear entrance.

Toby looked down at the book he was carrying as if he had forgotten it was there. At first, he seemed unable to give a response which made Natalie step in to answer her own question.

"Are you planning to teach Micha geography?" she teased with a forgiving smile.

"Sort of. Well not really. I mean... well I just thought she might like to see where her dad came from," his answer made Toby immediately regret his decision to bring the book and left him suddenly feeling very foolish, a feeling that his cheeks chose to share with the rest of the world.

"Good idea. Micha likes looking at pictures from around the world. I didn't know you knew where Sundance was from." The final comment sounded a bit like an accusation as if Toby was getting ideas above his station. Natalie was still coming to terms with the reality of the situation, that Toby was now part of Micha's world; a world that until two days ago had a population of just two.

Toby told Natalie about his reading last night and what he already knew about Sundance. She was pleased with how passionate Toby was becoming about Micha's world and was reassured once more that she had done the right thing in letting him into their secret.

Toby explained how he wanted to get all the apes relocated back to the Bili-Uele region and how he planned to do it. Natalie had been letting them both into the enclosure as they chatted and had not really been paying attention to what was happening the other side of the fence, in the chimpanzees' living quarters. It was not until Toby placed his atlas on the floor and was through the first of the double lock gates that they both spotted Sundance sitting cross-legged, his massive arms resting in his lap staring with intense fury at them both.

It really was a breath-taking sight to receive the full focus of Sundance's attention. He was an enormous chimpanzee, almost full adult human size but perhaps five times as strong. Sundance was much more comfortable than most apes when standing on two feet as he would often do if he needed to intimidate any potential rival. His face bore several scars, reminders of a childhood in the harsh realities of the wild and the more recent hard-won supremacy for his alpha status. His gaze was an unforgiving one and was locked on Toby. Two pin-prick black pupils centred in his fiery orange eyes, set deep beneath his colossal brow that gave the appearance of an oncoming set of car headlights speeding from a darkened tunnel, a warning that an impact was inevitable.

Cowering in the background, head in her lap, arms folded up to protect herself was Micha. She crouched silently but was gently rocking back and forwards shaking her head from side to side as if she was trying to convince herself that something really hadn't happened, although clearly it had.

Natalie reacted with a calm professionalism that years of training had given her. She watched Sundance intently, scanning him for any slight twitch or shift in position that might signal an attack. Despite her acute concentration, she was becoming dimly aware of a recognisable sound coming from the back of the enclosure, a repeated and clearly defined word was coming from Micha.

"Sorry."

Natalie broke her attention from Sundance and shifted it to Micha, shocked and confused that she would be speaking to them in front of the other apes. She called out to her.

"Micha darling, are you OK? You don't ever speak in front of your family, remember? What's the matter darling, what has happened?"

The questions had all been rhetorical from Natalie; she didn't expect or even want a reply, she was happy with Micha's decision to remain mute in front of her kind and didn't see any reason to change it. But there was no disguising or denying the response that she got.

"I'm sorry Natalie, I'm sorry." Micha had raised her head from her lap and was crying the words out, the pain clear in her voice and on her face. Her lip was swollen, and there was a cut above her eye. "They made me tell them what we have been doing. Kianza had heard me talking to you and had told our father. They beat me, and I was frightened it would get much worse. I told them all about you and me and how Toby knows now as well."

It was Natalie's turn to be furious now, the sight of her beloved Micha's injuries, were more than she could bear. She cried out to Micha to reassure her and to say she would get her out of there as quick as they could but before she could finish her sentence the volcano erupted.

Sundance exploded to his feet, a raging inferno, towering over Toby but now launching himself at Natalie. His uncontrolled frenzy of wrath burst out of him as he tore at the fence, ripping at the mesh with his fingers and pounding his fists until they bled; all the while roaring and screeching with such an indignant fury that both Toby and Natalie covered their ears and turned their heads unable to face the terrifying onslaught. The yellow of his eyes glowed like vents into a furnace, and the muscles in his vast shoulders and arms strained at his skin as if they might burst from an ill-fitting suit. He was pulling at the fence with both arms, using his feet as a fulcrum so he could lean back to get the maximum weight and leverage with each pull. There was no question that the fence was being tested to its limit and the injuries to his hands and feet were getting worse with open cuts forming on all of Sundance's fingers and toes.

Natalie had no choice but to get the hose and unleash its full power on the great ape. She hated to do it and had to force herself to watch as the icy jet hit Sundance in his chest and then his face. The effect was almost instantaneous. He fell from the fence and rolled away across the floor slapping his palms against the wet concrete and screeching his bitter resentment as he went.

Micha had not sat still during the attack but had used the diversion to climb the back wall of the enclosure. She was perched on the highest nesting platform her head only just visible as he peeked over the edge to watch the battle unfold beneath her. Once the hose was off and she had checked that Toby was unharmed, Natalie called out to Micha, a frightened mum searching for their lost child after the storm has cleared.

"Micha! Micha! It's OK darling you can come out now; we are all fine. Sundance has gone now; please come over here I want to check your injuries, see how badly you're hurt. Come on darling; it's safe now."

"Safe! Are you mad? What part of safe don't you two understand?"

Chapter 15
The Walk

Dan Potter was staring into the abyss when Jack walked in on him.

He hadn't got dressed yet and hadn't washed or shaved since the morning of his wife's funeral. His sunken cheeks and weary eyes showed how little he had eaten or slept since then as well. Jack stopped in the doorway when he saw Dan crumpled at the breakfast bar, a full cup of coffee sat cold and untouched in front of him. This moment of hesitation gave Jack time to recall, however briefly, just what a beautiful couple Dan and Alice had been.

Jack was twelve when his older sister brought her boyfriend home for tea for the first time. Dan was a happy chancer of a kid from the side of the estate where Alice and Jack were not supposed to go. But Dan had enough charm to keep him on the right side of cocky and enough humility to keep him on the right side of arrogant: Jack liked him immediately. His sister Alice had always been Jack's North Star, his guiding light that told him the road to follow when his head and heart couldn't figure out which way up to hold the map. Both

Dan and Jack had benefited from this constant uplift of hope and encouragement. Alice driving them on like a turbofan to the limits of their full potential. For Dan that meant driving him from his North London, council estate poverty of charity clothes and school lunch often the only meal of the day to unassailable wealth in under thirty years. Jack knew that Dan was in a tailspin, free falling without his driving wind, his rudder or his safety net. There was no way he could leave him like this.

"Get dressed, mate, you're coming with me."

The firmness of Jack's grip left Dan in no doubt that he would need to do as he was told. It felt good to him to be able to surrender control, to sense the clutch of a saving hand pulling him from his despair.

Jack didn't really have a plan, but he knew that the best thing to do was to show Dan that the world had not stopped turning and to remind him just how much those around him needed to feel his presence. By getting Dan out of the house and into the park, he was sure that he could start him on the long slow journey to recovery.

Without knowing where to start a conversation, Jack did what he always did and started talking about the animals under their care.

"Achilles is getting lonely. He needs a mate. I have been checking in with the species co-ordinator on the lion database every week, but there is nothing that fits just yet. Poor bugger, I know just how he feels."

They were walking past Achilles who was in a

familiar pose, flat on his side with four legs stretched out in front of him, and his head arched back, eyes closed with the occasional twitch of his tail being the only reliable sign of life. Dan gazed through the glass partition envying Achilles his loneliness, knowing that he could never go back to a time when he didn't love Alice, could never go back to a time when he would just be alone and be spared the torture of missing his wife every second of every day. He was about to speak, to tell Jack that he was going back to the cottage, but Jack was in lecture mode, using his words like cavity wall insulation, forcing them into any space in the conversation hoping they would expand and fill any awkward silences.

"Mind you, if Omar doesn't work his magic on Salma this time around, I think I'll let Achilles into the tiger enclosure and maybe we can have a little liger as our next attraction."

Jack turned to Dan, hoping to see maybe a glimmer of recognition for what he had said, but all he was met with was a blank, disconnected stare.

"Dan, mate; I know I am just noise in the background right now, but I'm just trying to fill in some of the gaps for you. Silence is where the bad things happen. If you crawl back into your dark place, you may never come back out, and too many people need you right now, buddy. Toby needs you. I need you. Everyone at the zoo needs you. You and me, are going to miss Alice every single day for the rest of our lives, but that mustn't be all we do. I loved my sister, and you loved your wife, and that will be true until the day we die, but between now and that day I want to live every day honouring her memory. I want to fill each hour with a life that she would be proud of. And one of the few things that I am sure of Dan, my man, is that she would have never wanted me to leave you behind. You're not my brother-in-law any more Dan, you're my brother, and I love you, and I want to help you, anyway I can."

Jack had been pulling in Dan closer to him with each word, and Dan was now resting his head on Jack's shoulder, an act of total surrender — an admission of an inability to take even another step unaided.

They sat for five minutes in that pose, Jack recognising the need for silence and Dan unable to speak. Eventually, though the words came to him and Dan sat up, turning to face Jack and weak smile of gratitude starting to creep cautiously to the corners of his mouth.

"Thank you, Jack. You always were my brother; Alice told me that from the start. She wanted us to be close, and I was happy with that. You're right; I know you're right. I can't wallow in pity all day but God, Jack, I miss her. It's killing me and what kills me, even more, is to think how much Toby must be suffering right now. No boy should ever have to go through this, losing his mum; it's the worst Jack, worse than losing a wife or a sister. He can never ever be her son again, and it makes me want to scream and cry and bash my 'ead with a brick, just to try and take away some of his pain. There is nothing I wouldn't do for that boy, and I would give everything I own to make him happy again, but I don't know where to begin. 'Ow can I Jack? 'Ow can I help him? The only thing that is going to get me through this is knowing that I did the right thing for Toby."

Dan was almost pleading with Jack, begging for the answer that might make all this right for him; give him a purpose where none could be seen. Jack was relieved to see the passion in Dan's eyes but couldn't for the life him think what to say next, what answer to give Dan that might feed this new desire. He had no idea why he did it, but he just started talking about Micha.

"Toby has been spending lots of time over there with Natalie at the ape arena. They are both pretty smitten with the young female chimpanzee Micha. Matter of fact I was chatting about her to both of them, and they think we need to relocate them back to the wild. I think Toby would really like your help with this".

"Get rid of the chimps? Are you mad Jack? The punters love 'em, the little ones, most of all. That Micha is a prize ticket. Maybe get rid of some of the older ones that sit around doing nothing all day, or that little sod that keeps throwing his poo at the window every time a bunch of school kids pass by."

Both of them were laughing now. It was Kianza

who was guilty of this particular habit, and it was alarming just how good a shot he was; nine times out of ten he could hit the spot where some unsuspecting schoolboy (it was always the boys) had pushed his face against the window pane to make monkey noises at them.

"You can't just split a family up like that Dan. Chimpanzees are highly intelligent social animals who make bonds for life."

"Jeez Jack, I know you and Natalie love these animals like they're your own, but they are only animals — we can split them up if we have to and Toby will get over it, give him a week, and he will have forgotten Micha's name."

The talk of business had suddenly given Dan the distraction he needed. It wasn't just happy luck that had let Dan make as much money as he had over the years. His incredible eye for detail and an uncanny knack at guessing what the markets would do had allowed Dan to build up an investment fund worth billions by the time he was thirty-five. When he had sold the fund and the family home in London to move to the zoo, Dan had amassed a fortune that would be impossible for him, or Toby or the next two generations of Potters, at least, to spend. It wasn't that Dan loved money, or even really liked it, he just understood it better than most people and never wanted to see it wasted.

"Come on Jack we need to get a move on, I need to

get back to the office before the park opens and you need to get to work. These animals aren't going to treat themselves, mores the pity; it'd save me a fortune in vets' bills. And don't worry about Toby and Micha; If I know my son, he's already got a new favourite animal and wouldn't recognise that Micha if she fell on him."

On this parting note, Jack and Dan had left the bench and were heading towards the exit of the Jungle Zone, just as Natalie and Toby turned the corner around the back of the ape enclosure with Micha swinging happily between them both.

Toby and Natalie were each holding one of Micha's hands with the chimpanzee looking up at them and laughing as she swung from their arms her feet skipping across the floor as she hurried to keep pace with them.

Chapter 16
The Talk

It had taken Natalie and Toby half an hour to coax Micha back down from her perch following the attack by her father and almost as long again to get her to say a word to them.

Eventually, though, she had sat beside Toby who had not moved from the fence since the attack had ended, Micha put her hand up to the mesh but kept her head bowed and gaze averted until they were holding hands through the wire in their now familiar pose. Toby spoke first,

"Micha, are you hurt at all? We were so worried about you and your father."

"My father? Sundance the Mighty Jungle Warrior? He is not worried about a few scratches; he has suffered far worse from humans in the past; he doesn't need anyone's help. He just needs to live in a world without wire fences and metal cages, same as me. Those are the wounds that need healing."

Natalie had used the time to come up with an idea.

"Micha darling, I need to go to my office to get some antibiotics to give to Achilles for his toothache, he has an abscess. Would you like to come with me?"

Natalie dropped the last question in like she was asking Micha if she had had enough breakfast. It was delivered as a passing comment almost not worthy of a reply, but the words had dropped into her lap like the longed-for rains hitting a parched desert plain. She forgot all pretence of sullen injury and jumped up and down hooting and screeching with excitement, unable to think of the human words that might express her excitement half as well as her chimpanzee calls could.

"Sssh, Micha, we don't want Sundance or Kianza coming to see what the fuss is. I am going to get one of the support harnesses from the sick bay so we can help you walk with us. You stay here with Toby, and he will tell you about what you will see when you get out there."

Micha could not believe that she would be going outside of the enclosure. Her lifelong wish had come like a bolt from the blue and was going to happen right now.

"I'm going outside Toby; I'm going to be free. I'm going to see the other side of the bars. Do you know what this means? Do you know how I feel?" Toby felt ashamed to say that he didn't know how she felt. He had never been locked away with his life under someone else's total control, other than his parents he guessed. He thought about Micha's glass walled arena and the fishbowl flat he had grown up in but there really was no comparison. Toby felt like they both needed a distraction

"Which animal would you like to see most of all when you get outside?"

"Achilles, definitely Achilles, I have heard him roar so many times and have never seen him. And then the penguins. I want to see them swim, that'll be amazing. Del Boy and Rodney tell me all about them, how they like to gossip and bicker all day and argue over who ate the most fish, they sound so funny. Ooh and the tortoises and the tigers and the lemurs and the Camels and..."

"OK, OK, I get it, you want to see them all."

Natalie rushed back in puffing a little from her sprint across to the sick bay. She was carrying what looked like a baby harness that parents make toddlers wear sometimes, only much, much stronger. Natalie explained that it was to go around her chest to help them hold her up if her legs got tired.

Micha was holding both Toby and Natalie's hands when they lead her out through the back door of the enclosure and onto the lawn that lay behind. She couldn't hold back a squeal when her toes curled into the, fresh cut grass, still wet with dew and not yet warmed by the sun. She let go of them both to reach down and pick up a hand full of blades, letting them fall from her hands into the wind.

Natalie and Toby laughed in shared joy at the impact this adventure was having on their dear friend.

It had been so easy for both of them to assume that Micha was happy in her cage and would prefer to be inside with her family rather than outside here with them. Like everyone who visits a zoo, they had been able to tell themselves that the animals don't want to be free they just want to be fed and have somewhere to sleep at night.

"OK little lady, where are we going first?" Natalie asked.

"Achilles please, I can't wait to see him," Micha chirped between them, every inch the excited school girl on her first trip to the zoo, rather than the wild animal she was, on her way to confront a mortal enemy.

Natalie and Toby laughed again, and Micha joined in with a squeak as she jumped over a puddle, using both her friends to lift her up and swing her over the water. In the next moment, however, it was Natalie's turn to let out a squeak when they rounded the enclosure and walked straight into not only Jack but also Toby's dad, the owner of the zoo and her boss.

All four humans stared at each other in stunned silence, uttering not one meaningful syllable between them for what seemed like a timescale of geological proportions. Natalie had been caught red-handed breaking one of the zoo's most important rules — no large animals out of their enclosures without strict supervision from three trained keepers.

Toby broke the silence in the end by letting go of

Micha's hand and rushing over to his dad and taking his instead.

"Dad, you have got to see this. Natalie has let me walk one of the apes. She was taking her to sickbay to look at a cut on her head and couldn't find any of the other keepers so she asked if I would help. I went to get the harness for her, and Natalie showed me how to put it on, and now we are taking her to the offices. How cool is that?"

"Is that safe Natalie? That's my boy you've got there, and he was with a wild animal. Who knows what might happen?"

Dan might have bought the zoo but at no point did he ever consider it necessary for him to learn what animals were in it or what they were called. Right now, though he wished he had maybe even just glimpsed at the visitors' brochure as he wasn't entirely sure if that was a monkey or an ape or what the difference was. He would really have felt better knowing if that creature holding his son's hand was a veggie or a meat eater.

Jack had plenty of concerns of his own as well.

"It's safe for Toby, Dan but I am a bit worried about Micha; how bad is the cut? How did it happen? Should she be walking to sickbay or do we need to assess here? You should have come to get me, Natalie; you know that this is my decision to make not yours."

"It's a minor cut. It was caused by a scuffle with Sundance and Kianza and knowing Kianza's habits there is a fair chance that his hands were not clean. It looked like it might have been a bite from Sundance that did it so at the very least I wanted to clean it out. You know we've talked about how cramped they are getting in there, fights like this are going to become much more common so getting Micha out for a little time on her own seemed like the best option."

"You could have come looking for me or sent Toby, I would have come straight away to help. And I know how cramped things are. We've talked about relocating Micha and her family, I was just talking to Dan about it. He agrees with me; it is probably best to split the family up and maybe keep Micha for the time being at least."

Natalie gasped at the news Jack was sharing with them. Micha was terrified by the news that her family might be split up and sent away from the zoo, it was like she had overheard someone discussing her death sentence. She was becoming increasingly more agitated and was starting to open her mouth wide and swing her head from side to side silently at first but soon with an increasingly loud "Ak, Ak," sound from the back of her throat. Natalie used it as a much-needed excuse to get them both out of the situation.

"Micha is getting bored with our chat. I think I should take her to sick bay as planned. You can come if you want Jack, but I am sure all it needs is a gentle clean up; I will call if you I need you. Toby, are you coming?"

She did not wait for anyone to answer but headed off in the direction of the offices, picking Micha up as she went, using the opportunity to whisper to her.

"Don't worry Micha; I will explain everything when we are out of earshot. No one is going to split your family up. I've got to take you to sick bay now, or Jack will get suspicious. I will pretend to clean your cut up and then we can take a slow walk back to the arena."

"Actually, I think you should clean my cut," whispered Micha "Kianza's hands weren't very clean."

Natalie laughed out loud as Micha nuzzled her head into her shoulder and Toby put his hand in hers, squeezing it as he did.

Chapter 17
The Squark

Natalie was right to take Micha to the sick bay as Jack joined them five minutes later, having made his excuses to Dan.

Micha's cut actually did need cleaning out, and she was being brave in letting Natalie swab it with an antiseptic wipe. To his horror, Toby was put on grooming duty to relax Micha and was stood behind her making a very half-hearted attempt at searching her hair for nits and bugs. Natalie glanced up as Jack walked in a gave him a welcoming smile which had a hint of "told you so" about it.

"How is she doing?"

"Oh, Micha's just fine, not sure about Toby though, he may have had better days."

She winked at Toby as she said this, making him laugh despite his current position as Chief Nit Picker.

Jack wanted to continue their talk about the plans for the chimpanzees and started to talk about the dynamic in the troop. Micha was able to keep quiet, but she did manage a perfectly timed eye roll at Natalie when she was sure that Jack was not watching.

Natalie was worried that Jack might start going into details about how they could split the troop up, but she was well aware of the effect that she had on Jack and was not above using it to her advantage.

One hit with her best smile and holding eye contact with him for five seconds more than was strictly necessary for polite conversation was all Natalie needed. Jack backed out of the sick bay knocking a trolley into the filing cabinet and sending a surgical tray to the floor as he went. He stumbled as he crouched to pick up the instruments and knocked his head on the doorknob as he turned to leave. By Jack's standards, this was quite an elegant exit.

Once Natalie was sure that she had seen Jack head over to the cottage she led Toby and Micha out of the sick bay and back up the path to the Jungle Zone knowing they had only a few minutes before the park would open to visitors.

Achilles was in his usual repose, flat on his side like a deflated lion balloon rather than the magnificent creature that he was. His lack of animation did not seem to dampen Micha's excitement one little bit. As soon as Achilles was in Micha's line of sight she pulled away from Natalie and Toby's hand holds and rushed to the glass wall that ran the perimeter of the moat around his den. She pressed her face against the glass, drinking in every last drop of the view. She stayed silent for only a few seconds before she began making a series of low, rumbling grunts, quite unlike any of her normal chimpanzee sounds Natalie was used to hearing.

The effect was almost instantaneous; Achilles lifted his enormous head from the ground and stared straight at Micha. Toby didn't have time to gasp at the speed at which the mighty lion had got to his feet and cleared the ground between them. Any doubts that Toby had held about how deadly a lion in the wild might be were fully and emphatically resolved. He suddenly knew what it is was like to be the centre of a lion's attention and it was the most exhilarating experience that he had ever known; electricity crackled through his hair and his teeth and his nails like sparks might fly from them.

Micha kept up her low, sonorous rumble, never once breaking eye contact with Achilles, who kept up his slow dance of side-to-side steps, all the while holding his head and gaze firmly fixed forward on the trio in front of him. After a perhaps half a minute of Micha's rumblings Achilles began his reply; an impossibly deep, guttural reverberation that sounded like two enormous boulders being rubbed together.

The sounds juddered in Natalie and Toby's chest so that it registered in their bones before their ears could make sense of it.

Once the vibrations had made it to their brains every cell in their bodies had been put on red alert, long dormant alarms signals firing in every muscle, triggered by the deep parts of the nervous system that kept humans alive when they were at the bottom of the food chain, not the top. The words spoken between the ape and the lion meant nothing to the humans present but the depth and volume of the sounds coming from Achilles certainly told them who was in charge.

"What do you want, ape?" The final word, ape, was said with venom, intended as an insult, not a title.

"Don't be rude, Prowler, I have come to see you to tell you who I am and what I am going to do."

"I already know who you are — a tree rat and I don't care what you are going to do."

"I am Micha, daughter of Sundance and I am going to set my family free."

Achilles snapped his head back and roared, his mouth an enormous gaping cavern that revealed a vast carnivorous black hole. He had stiffened his hind legs and dug his claws into the ground as if he was bracing himself for the recoil his roar was going to create as it left his body. The sound shook the glass wall in front of them and caused all three of them to take an involuntary step back. The roar ricocheted around the park, bouncing from pen to pen waking every occupant from the last vestiges of sleep and causing legs to twitch and limbs to stiffen as each animal took notice of their primordial responses.

"Free! Free? What do you know of being free, Tree Rat? You think you are free because the No Hairs let you walk around with them? You stand there tied to

144

them and talk to me about freedom? I walked the mighty plains with my family before the hunters came, hunters like the ones you are standing next to now. They took me, and they left my family to die just so they could make me dance for them."

"I am sorry for your family but these No Hairs are my friends…"

"You are a fool Tree Rat. The No Hairs have forgotten that they were once one of us; they think they rule us all now. They will never be your friend. If you want me to help you, push them over that wall, and I will kill them both for you, then you can go and hide in a tree until they find you. That is all the freedom you will ever know."

"You are wrong, Prowler, killing the No Hairs will not help us. I must teach them what they have forgotten; this is what I must do, and you can tell me much about the land you came from and how the No Hairs behave there. I will visit you again, and we will talk more. I have a plan. You will see that I am right."

Achilles seemed to dismiss Micha with a flick of his tail and a shrug of his colossal mane. He turned and slunk away to the corner of his grassy plot beneath the large oak tree at the back of the pen, as far away from the excited visitors who would soon be lining the glass wall where Natalie, Toby and Micha stood now.

Natalie signalled that it was time to head back to the ape arena. Toby knew that an important conversation had taken place and was keen to find out what had been said. For her part though, Natalie, was blissfully unaware of anything other than standard threat assessment and responses being made by two animals encountering each other for the first time.

"Come on Micha we can talk all you want when we get you back inside."

"I don't feel like talking much now." Toby knew that something had been said between Micha and Achilles that had upset her and he was desperate to find out what. He knew he would have to bribe her though.

"I might have something that might change your mind"

Micha looked up at Toby.

"If you want me to talk, you had better have some cake," she said as she took hold of Toby's hand and let go of her grip on the glass wall.

In the trees above her, Del Boy and Rodney had been watching the whole episode. They had watched Micha speak to the two humans in the same language as them and then heard of her plans from the conversation with Achilles. In unison, the two parrots began to squawk.

"Micha speaks! Micha speaks."

Chapter 18
Toby Learns about Sundance

Natalie and Toby had got Micha back to the enclosure just a couple of minutes before the park gates opened.

They had gone more or less straight back from the meeting with Achilles with only a small detour to allow her to see the rest of the big cats. Micha had been fascinated by the cheetahs and their cub, but when she heard that they had all been born in captivity, she seemed to lose interest and wanted to move on. They had passed the two tigers, Omar and Salma but Micha had paid them as little attention as they had paid her.

Micha was tired from her long walk and by the time they got back to the enclosure she made it clear to Natalie and Toby that she was ready for a nap and was not interested in any more chat. Natalie was quick to leave her to it, but Toby had nowhere else to be, and was happy enough to sit with his back against the fence and talk to an empty room, satisfied that there was some slim chance that Micha was still listening.

"I was surprised that you wanted to see the big cats most of all today, Micha. I thought you would have wanted to see the gibbons or the mandrills, or the lemurs. You know, someone, a bit more like you... I'm not saying you're a monkey." Toby was quick to add this bit, remembering his first meeting and the stern warning he'd received that day.

"We have a family of mandrills here at the park; they are from Congo just like you, well you know what I mean, just like your dad. They came to us here when their part of the jungle was burned down by farmers; they've only been with us for a few weeks. We've got some barbary macaque as well nearly twenty now, with a new baby due next week. Boy do they fight a lot, they make your family look positively normal. We've also got some sphinx night monkeys as well, from South America, Guyana, I think. We hardly ever see them though, they sleep more than Achilles. I think they look like Dad looks if he doesn't have a coffee in the morning, but they look like that all day. I said gibbons, didn't I? Well, we have six of them; they're apes as well like us, aren't they? Not quite like us though, not one of the great apes, eh?"

Toby threw his head back when he said this and checked over his shoulder to see if there had been any response, but Micha was flat out on her perch, one arm hanging loosely over the edge and there was not the slightest sign of interest coming from up there. Toby carried on regardless.

"Jack told me that Achilles was in a circus before he came to us; that must have been so weird for him. To go from being a wild beast, King of the Jungle and all that, to doing tricks for kids in a big tent. Jack said they called him Roary! Can you imagine that? How embarrassing Roary the lion, like a stuffed toy."

Toby was laughing at the thought of it, but then he remembered the roar this morning. Was that a cry of rage and pain, was it angry screaming like he did two weeks ago in the hospital as he lay on top of his mum? The memory of that morning forced its way into his head like a bully pushing his way to the front of the queue. Uninvited and unstoppable the images filled his head, and the tears flowed without hesitation. He was alone, so he let them flow, unashamed this time, no one there to see his weakness. The speed and intensity of the intrusion had taken him completely by surprise. From laughter to tears in a heartbeat with no control over either. When he spoke next, it was quieter. A mumbled scatter of thoughts aimed at no one, but he needed them out of his head.

"Do animals miss their mums? Did Achilles have a family back home? Did he have kids and a wife and a mum and dad? I miss my mum so much, and it's only been two weeks. She could have been away that long on holiday only I know I will never see her again. No matter how long I live, I will never ever hear her voice again or feel her skin against my face when she kisses me goodbye in the morning. Is that how your dad feels Micha, does Sundance think about his family? He was an orphan, wasn't he? Did he miss his mum like I miss mine? Was he frightened when he was all alone?

I'm all alone right now Micha; you're my only friend. Jack and Natalie are grown-ups, Dad is my dad, and I don't know anyone else, not really. You're all I've got Micha, and sometimes I'm not sure you're even real. Do I have a friend who is a talking chimpanzee? Or am I just going mad? I want to talk to all the animals like you can. I want to hear what it is like to be a bird or a crocodile. I want to know what the lemurs are thinking about when they sunbathe, what the penguins talk about all day. I don't know why Micha, but I think I was supposed to meet you. Like I am here to help you. I've no idea how I can, but I know I will."

Toby felt like he had finished talking like he'd cleared out all the lurking thoughts that were hanging around in the corners of his mind; got them out into the open where they didn't look so big or scary. He was ready to get up and head back to the cottage for some breakfast when he felt the thick, coarse skin of Micha's palm press through the fence and stroke gently across the back of his head.

When he turned to face her, they were eye to eye, less than a foot apart.

Toby stared into her bright brown eyes, eyes that seemed to have softened, showing a hint of sadness mixed with an aura of empathy and understanding that was reinforced by a crinkling of the deep ridges in her heavy brow. For a moment Toby thought he was looking into the eyes of a kindly old woman. He saw Micha as a human, not an animal; he felt as if he had met, for the first time, a sister he never knew he had. They were no longer human and chimpanzee, they were two Apes sharing a moment before they started a great journey together. For an instant, the bars and the wire fences disappeared, and they were merely two friends sat together; a brother and a sister bridging a gap of six million years since they would have last been able to be siblings for real.

"Dad thinks of his family every day; he saw them all get killed when he was a little boy. That's why he hates humans, well that's one of the reasons. He watched them kill his family and was tortured by them in a cage for twenty years. He hates you all. In that mood, if he could have got through this fence, he would have killed you both without hesitation. Kianza is the same; he does everything that dad tells him to. He's grown up being told every day that No Hairs are the vilest animal ever. Dad thinks his jungle home is just the other side of the trees that he can see from the arena; he has no idea how far away he is. He wants to get back there and never see a human again. I told him that being able to talk to you is a good thing, that you will help us get back there; but he will never trust you or Natalie or Jack. It doesn't make any difference to him who you are or what you are like. You are human; a No Hair and you are the enemy. He doesn't want me to speak to you ever again."

The enormity of what she had just said hit them both at the same time. Suddenly the threat from Sundance became very real.

Toby knew he was safe on his side of the bars, that Sundance or Kianza would never be able to get to him. But he was worried about Micha and realised at that moment that she would have to do whatever she was told to do. Micha could see the impact her words were having on Toby.

"You have to get us out of here soon, or I will never be allowed near you again. I have to go into the arena now and see what the rest of the troop thinks about me. But before I go back in, tell me about the mandrills."

Chapter 19
Micha's Not Welcome

From the morning of that first walk around the zoo with Micha, Toby had eight weeks of summer holidays before he started at his new school; he spent every single morning and evening with Micha.

Natalie had seen how much the walk had meant to Micha after that first morning and all three agreed that it should happen as often as possible. Micha was not happy at all about the idea of the leash and gave an impressive display of a full-blown teenager tantrum when she was told she needed to wear one. Although she eventually tolerated it, she never missed an opportunity to pull a sulking face when it was fitted and would make no effort to help them put her "noose" on as she took to calling it.

At first, the walks were chosen by Micha as she said which animals she would like to visit.

Not all of the animals in the zoo had enough language skills or intellect to work out what was being said or what it meant, but all the larger land mammals could communicate to a high level as could the birds and most of the larger reptiles.

One of the first walks had been to see the mandrills, and it seemed that Micha had much to discuss as she asked to revisit them at least once a week from then on. There were just three mandrills, a family consisting of an older male, Kalala who had only just established a role as a dominant male so was enjoying his new unchallenged state, his mate Santu and their young son, Alongi.

Micha had been very excited to meet the three mandrills, but Kalala and Santu were apparently not keen to talk to a chimpanzee, showing the natural wariness that all animals of the Congo show to these sometimes-violent apes.

In the wild chimpanzees will occasionally kill and eat other monkeys, mainly red colobus monkeys and while it is doubtful that they would take on the much more formidable mandrills, they would not be above killing an infant one if they found it. The chimpanzees of the Congo have a fearsome reputation for brutal enforcement of their territory, so it was not surprising that Santu scooped Alongi up and took him to the safety of their wooden shelter.

Kalala took up a threatening stance at the border of his land gaping his massive jaws wide, so they covered the outline of Micha's reflection in the glass wall that surrounded them. Micha knew enough from Sundance's bragging about the reputation of her kind in the wild, to understand why Kalala was acting as he did. She took up her familiar pose of meek surrender to show that she was no threat to him or his family.

Toby and Micha had to be patient and let Kalala go through his full display, but after five minutes of passive submission by them both he relented and took up a position of guarded tolerance, placing himself firmly between the two intruders and his family, his face almost touching the glass pane.

"What do you want Monkey Eater? There is no food for you here,"

"I am no monkey eater; I came to talk to you Sky Face, I want to learn about my home, the land where you have come from. I want to lead my family back there, and I need your help."

Toby spent many hours over those summer months at meetings like this one and while he never managed to understand what the animals were saying he was able to pick out specific sounds that became more familiar to him. When he coupled these with what Micha repeated from the conversations, and by observing her body language, he did eventually develop a slight insight into how they communicated and how the discussions were going. This early on, however, he was clueless, even failing to notice when the animals' attention had turned to him as they discussed humans and what they were doing to their lands in the wild.

"KijaniKubwa The Big Green? What do you care about that place? I am glad to be free of it. If the No

Hairs are not burning it down, you Monkey Eaters are killing off every animal that enters your lands. I am glad to leave, we will never go back, and I am happy. The parrots have told us about you and about that little No Hair. We do not want to help you, and we do not want to be part of any plan of yours."

Santu had come out of the closed shelter but had left Alongi hidden inside.

"What does the Monkey Eater want? Why is she here with a No Hair?"

"She wants us to help her get to the KijaniKubwa. She thinks she can climb under The Big Green Blanket, thinks it will keep her safe and warm. She thinks its big strong green arms will wrap around her and lift her high into its mighty trees so all animals there can worship her."

"Look at her; she has never been to the wild. She does not know that death waits for her on every branch and under every plant. She cannot know what hunger is. She has never been hunted, been fearful that she will not live to see another moment. That is why she wants to go there because she has no idea what is there. She is a child, a foolish Monkey Eater who thinks she lives in the tallest tree. She is holding the No Hair's hand; she thinks they are friends. She does not know that the No Hairs eat chimpanzees just like they eat monkeys and every other animal in the Kubwa. Come Kalala, come back to our child with me, don't spend another moment with these two little fools'"

Santu had risen to full stretch and was standing on her hind legs with her paws on a perimeter bench so that she was taller than her mate now and even if she lacked his iridescent colours and formidable frame she suddenly seemed in charge of the situation; Kalala did not attempt to disagree. The two of them turned from Micha, not bothering with a parting shot or barbed farewell; preferring to leave her crestfallen and dejected rather than give her a chance to gain the final word.

Toby had no idea what words had been exchanged, but he sensed that the meeting had not gone well. As she watched the mandrills retreat to their home, Micha seemed to deflate slowly, like a flaccid party balloon; a crumpled remnant of some forgotten excitement.

Toby placed his hand on her shoulder, but as he did, he felt her body stiffen. Her already taught muscles bristled beneath her fur, coming alive like fire hoses filling under pressure. She rose high onto her hind legs as if she had just remembered who she was, Micha the Magnificent, Daughter of Sundance, The Warrior Princess. She looked up at Toby with what she hoped was an expression of defiant indifference. Despite her efforts, Micha was unable to hide the hurt that she had felt at Santu's words and the way all the animals so far had either rejected her, ignored her or hated her.

"I don't think chimpanzees are very popular in the wild. The monkeys are frightened of us, the lions don't

157

respect us, and the tigers can't even be bothered to acknowledge us."

"Welcome to my world Micha. I knew that humans weren't going to be too popular in the animal world, but I had no idea how despised we are. I think you are the only animal in this place who doesn't want to kill me or see me dead. You don't want to kill me do you, Micha?"

He smiled as he said this, but Micha kept him hanging on for an answer. She waited for the smile to leave and for worry and doubt to turn up and dig furrows across his brow before she let herself throw her head back and shriek with laughter, nodding furiously and slapping the ground with her open palms as she always did when she felt she had been particularly hilarious.

Toby felt like they needed a change of pace.

"Let's go try find an animal that doesn't hate us both."

Chapter 20
Micha Meets the Neighbours

And so it was for the whole of that brief, beautiful summer.

Micha and Toby touring the zoo, each taking it in turn, to choose which animal to visit and then spending time discussing the meeting afterwards, usually with Micha taking advantage of a nearby tree for a climb and a swing.

The summer evenings were kind to them that year, and Toby and Micha needed no encouragement to spend at least a part of each one sat on the banks of the Ponds that lay hidden within the woods.

Micha always seemed happy enough to spend a stolen moment or two with her human brother, lost in each other's thoughts, struck by the beauty and tranquillity of their surroundings. At these times, both of them were able to deny, however briefly, the existence of the bars and fences or boundaries and borders that kept their worlds forever separate.

Micha could stare into the water and believe the reflection looking back at her was that of a free ape living by the shores of the mighty Congo River, her troop waiting for her in the trees behind. Toby could look to the horizon and could catch fleeting glimpses of the passing cars between the tree-lined boundary as they hastened home and could allow himself to imagine that his mum was driving one and would be coming to call him for his tea soon. Micha learned to recognise this silent stare that usually led to a single tear and knew to leave him alone for a moment longer before signalling it was time to go. Eventually, though she would snap him out of it with her customary low hoot and a clap of her long, leathery palms before she tugged on her leash as if to confirm that it was her leading him and not the other way round.

When Toby got to choose an animal, he tried to move Micha away from the Jungle Zone. In their first week of walks, he took her to meet his favourite two characters, the world-famous Gertie and Bertie, two giant tortoises that had arrived as a gift from the Galapagos Islands shortly after the end of World War Two. Their exact age was not known, but they were believed to be over ninety years old making them the oldest inhabitants in the zoo.

They belonged to a species that had walked the earth for over eighty million years. This species had seen the dinosaurs come and go, had survived the mass extinction of sixty-five million years ago and lived undisturbed on the islands of the Galapagos for over a million years. It took humans less than a century from their first contact to nearly exterminate the entire species.

Albert and Gertrude had arrived by ship from their island home and were headline news when they landed at Southampton docks. The zoo gave them a pen the size of an average back garden that had been their home ever since.

If he wasn't in the ape enclosure then Toby was at his happiest when sitting in their garden with these two beautiful beasts, relaxing to the sound of the satisfied hum as they munched their way through their day-long meal of vegetarian delights.

Micha took a while to warm to this grand pair, but once she adjusted her speech and pace of life to theirs, she could see them for all their radiant serenity and always came away from a chat with them in a more reflective and philosophical mood than when she went in.

Toby was desperate to hear about their lives and practically dragged Micha into their garden the first time they went to meet them.

"Can you ask them about how it was, coming to England from the Galapagos Islands? What did they think was happening?"

Micha began her deep, throaty grunts and murmurings that Toby would learn to recognise as the first, opening paragraph at any attempt to speak across species. He thought of it like someone trying to tune into

161

the right radio station, like both animals needed to know which frequency to use before they started speaking. She had to try a couple of times and eventually realised that Bertie was replying, but she had to lean in very close and concentrate fully on his voice before she could make any sense of the reply. The words came in very slow and very low, at a pitch almost below what Toby and Micha could hear at all.

Gertie and Bertie talked in the form of a relay, each one picking up the last word of the other's sentence like a baton.

"We were glad to be away from the rats; they kept eating our eggs. Of course, we worried that the humans were going to…"

"Eat us. We were worried they would eat us; we had heard so many tales of humans eating tortoises and knew that they used to take many, many, many, of us away on ships and we would never…"

"See them again. We would never see them again."

"When we got here, they put us in this garden, and we figured they would eat us sooner or later. Of course…"

"They never did, and now we know they don't do that any more. We like it here; we love our…"

"Garden. We love our garden. So many delicious leaves to eat and so many fine pieces of…"

"Fruit, so much fruit everywhere. Do you remember how it was when we came from the boat that brought us from our home Gertie, remember what it was like back on the island? We didn't like the rats, did we? They kept eating our…"

"…Eggs, they kept eating my eggs. Of course, we were worried that the humans were going to…"

And so, the slow, cautious conversation would repeat itself, an endless loop of half-remembered recollections and endlessly repeated anecdotes. Interspersed within these well-rehearsed dialogues.

Gertie, in particular, always managed to bring a certain grace to her thoughts. A tranquillity that gave gravitas to each word she delivered making them often seem more like she was donating a treasured family heirloom; Micha received these gifts with great gratitude each time Gertie shared one with her.

Often Gertie would tell Micha about life in her world where a male and a female could mate for life and not have to fight each other for status every day. This was a world so alien to her that she understood less about it then she did about Toby's life of TVs and laptops. She would talk to Micha about what she felt was her duty in life — to bear the burden of her captivity by filling every day with love.

"I can spend every day thinking about the fences that surround me or I can fill the space around me with love; the choice is mine alone, and I have to make it every day."

Love is not an emotion that chimpanzees pay much

attention to. Of course, a mother loves her children, and the friendships within the troop, especially amongst the females is an incredibly close one, but the idea of striving for peace and tranquillity and going at a pace of life that matched the speed of the plants that you eat all day made no sense to Micha.

Duty was a new thought to her as well; doing the right thing because it was what you should do not just what you wanted to do. She wanted to know more about this.

"Do you know what duty is, Toby? Do you have a duty? Is it your duty to keep me locked up or to help me be free?"

Toby had no reply at first for Micha; he was stunned by a question that showed so clearly both the innocence and the accusation that ruled so much of Micha's investigations. His lips moved wordlessly as though the air escaping from him had forgotten to pick up any syllables on the way from his lungs to his mouth.

His immediate answer would have been "to set you free," but then he thought about his dad, about the zoo, about the people who worked here, about what Jack had said. Did he not have a duty to them as well? Should he not think of them and their wishes before those of a young chimpanzee? Micha found her answer in the silence.

"If you don't know the answer Toby, then maybe you aren't the friend that I thought you were."

The sentence may have started out small, but once it was out of her mouth, the words seemed to expand, like a gas that has leaked into a room, filling the space between them, surrounding them with a bitter smell that lingered long after the end of their morning walk.

Chapter 21
Toby's Dilemma

It was a week since Micha had asked Toby about his duty and he still did not have an answer. If she had asked him, did he want her to be free then the, "Yes" would have been out of his mouth quicker than his lips could form the word. But what he wanted and what he thought was the right thing to do suddenly seemed like two ideas living on two different continents, each one slowly drifting away from the other.

Natalie had noticed an atmosphere between them and had teased them about having a "lover's tiff," a joke neither of them found remotely funny. Toby had sat with Natalie over her lunch after it happened and had asked her what he should do.

"I think duty is one of those things that finds you rather than the other way round."

"What is that supposed to mean Natalie? How do I know if it has found me? What if it doesn't ever find me, what do I do then?"

"What I mean is that you can't spend your days searching for your duty; you will just know it when you see it. We always know what the right thing to do is,

Toby; all of us do, it's just a question of whether we listen to the voice in our head or not. When the right thing to do presents itself to you, it will be obvious by how it makes you feel. If it seems impossible to do, if it scares you, makes you wish it would go away, but you still keep coming back to it and can never come up with a solid reason to not do it then it is probably the right thing to do. These thoughts usually come to you when you are not looking for them, at least that's what I've found."

The last bit made sense to Toby. He had always known for as long as could remember what the right thing to do was. Although Toby had grown up in a glass palace high above the streets of London both his parents had come from a very different background. They never missed an opportunity to remind him of the galaxy-sized gulf that existed between his life and the lives of others less fortunate than him.

Toby spent the week before his twelfth birthday wrestling with the dilemma Micha had left him with that morning; should he put the wishes and needs of Micha and her family ahead of his own? Jack and his dad had told him that the zoo needed Micha and the rest of the chimpanzees to keep the customers coming in. They were the star attraction and the money they brought in funded the rest of the animals, helping to keep them healthy and able to be put into breeding programs so their species could be saved from extinction. But knowing what he did about the animals now with Micha as his teacher could he be part of a world that kept them in cages so people could come and stare at them? Did the guests to the zoo leave after their visit feeling closer to the animals, thinking of them as equals or did they leave with an increased sense of their own worth, once again reassuring themselves that animals were primitive and dumb, OK for pets and eating but nothing more.

He had turned to Jack to help him with these thoughts.

"Do animals feel pain like we do?"

"Of course, they do Toby, pain is what helps keep us alive."

"What about love? Do Animals feel love like we do?"

"Oh boy, we are going deep today my friend. I think they do yes, but I can't prove it, and I'm not sure we ever will. When I watch the animals in here care for each other, feed their young, cuddle their babies, hug each other after fights I see that as love and in my world if you don't believe that, then you need to change your definition of love."

"So, if they feel pain and they can feel love, do they not suffer when we keep them in cages and take them away from the rest of their families?"

"OK Toby Wan Kenobi, where are you going with this? You know zoos aren't perfect, but we are doing the best we can. Humans have spent the last fifty thousand years hunting animals to extinction, and we aren't likely to stop anytime soon. If you are asking me if I think our animals suffer sometimes then yes, yes, they do. But at least they are alive and safe and cared for. I don't expect the rest of the world to treat animals as our equals, but the least we can do is treat with them kindness and respect. Who knows, if we do that then maybe we will want them as equals, and maybe, just maybe, they will think of us as equals as well. Now come on, enough with the deep stuff, let's talk rugby, right now they're the only Lions I'm interested in."

"Just one more question. Do you think different animals can talk to each other?"

"Tob-lerone! You are killing me with these questions." Jack laughed as he spoke. "I guess closely related species that inhabit similar environments may share sounds and calls that they both understand and can react to, but I don't think they can converse as we can. There was some research in California that looked at orcas and bottle nose dolphins in captivity, and it showed that both species changed their clicks and whistles, so they matched each other's, it seems that they could then teach each other how to solve puzzles. I guess that means they were talking to each other, on one level at least."

Jack had stood up and was starting to pace which meant he was getting into his stride on one of his favourite topics; Toby settled down on the sofa, happy to enjoy the ride.

"The mistake we make is that we think that our way of communicating is the best or only way of doing it, but that's rubbish. Ants and termites can communicate across colonies of up to a million animals using chemical messages that can mobilise the whole population in moments. The cuttlefish can flash messages across its whole-body using dozens of colours every second, and it can see with its entire body; it has photo-receptor cells in its skin as well as its eyes. We have to stop seeing the world through our eyes only and realise that the rest of the animal kingdom are highly-evolved specialist creatures every bit as developed as we are, and often more so. We have one central brain, and we are rightly very proud of it. But an octopus has been evolving their brain for millions of years longer than we have, and they have individual brains in each leg! Cephalopods could have ruled the world if they wanted to but they decided they were happier staying in the water, exploring the world with their nine different brains and three hearts. Yet we think we are the only intelligent life on earth? The arrogance of us, Toby. We are the ultimate drunk driver. About to drive the world off a cliff while ignoring every other passenger on board."

Toby could see that Jack was in the zone now so figured he may as well push on with a few more questions.

"So, we know that most animals can communicate with each other and you reckon some species can talk to each other so how come other animals don't talk like we do. How come other apes didn't evolve speech as we did."

"Yeah, that is a shame isn't I; I'd love to be able to sit and chat with our chimpanzees, how amazing would that be? Man, I could learn so much from them."

Toby did his best to hide his guilt as Jack said this but just kept quiet and let Jack carry on in lecture mode.

"Mind you, even if they could talk, we probably wouldn't understand them; their view of the world would be so different to ours that nothing they said would make any sense. I guess the real question is why have we not learned to speak to them? We haven't ever really managed to work out how animals are communicating which is our fault, not theirs. If all the chimpanzees can talk to each other in a way that allows them to thrive, then there was never any need for them to evolve a complex language like ours. It probably isn't down to brain size.

"Our brains are a fifth of the size they were thirty thousand years ago, and that hasn't stopped us talking nonsense for the whole of that time. There's a gene called the FoxP2 gene that we share with chimpanzees, but ours is switched on it controls about a hundred other genes that affect our ability to speak. It probably comes down to a mutation in this gene and us getting a long enough neck to allow the vocal cords to stretch enough and to get enough air over them, bits and pieces like that they gave us the ability to make loads more sounds."

"I bet if the animals in here could talk they ask to be set free."

"Change the story, Tobermory; we're not about to set all the animals free. Most of them would not survive, and the ones that could, well, they'll get relocated if we can find a suitable program. This isn't a prison mate; we keep them here to protect them not to punish them." Jack had sat back down next to Toby on the sofa and had pulled him in for a python-like squeeze. "Anyway, enough with the animals, what do you want for your birthday? It's in a week's time, so you might want to think of something."

"I don't want anything. I don't want to think about it."

"I know that mate, and I know why, but your dad needs to do something for you, he

is hurting so bad right now and the chance to make you happy, even just a tiny bit, is all that's keeping him going at the minute. Your mum wouldn't want you to miss out on your birthday. Just think of a little something that he can do for you. Please? Do it for your amazing Uncle Jack, before he crushes you to death."

Jack scooped Toby up off the sofa, tucked him under his arm and charged out of the cottage and into the park, pretending to dodge tacklers as he ran for the imaginary try line at the end of the garden.

Chapter 22
Mirror Mirror

Like most researchers who work with intelligent animals, Natalie had always seen chimpanzees as part of an extended human family and viewed any differences in behaviour as ones of degrees rather than kind.

She took the view that if we think that human intelligence and cognition are linked indivisibly with our consciousness, then it is reasonable to presume that this is true for other intelligent animals as well.

She knew that when she walked into the ape enclosure each morning, she was walking into the living room of an extended family just the same as when she walked into the cottage and sat with Jack, Dan and Toby.

Before Micha revealed her unique ability to her, Natalie had to make educated guesses about the mood of the troop and how welcoming they would be. Once Micha began to speak, however, she could tell Natalie about each member of the group and she was amazed at how well she had done at reading the cues. If they were smiling, they were happy, when the little ones were being tickled, they were laughing, when Sundance and Sally were kissing, they were making up after a row, and when Sundance looked like he wanted to rip your arms off you should probably choose another time to enter the enclosure.

Early on in their friendship Natalie had given Micha a mirror and asked the question that every animal behaviourist, psychologist and ethologist of the past two hundred years had wanted an answer to. "What do you see when you look in the mirror?"

"I see that my teeth are much more yellow than yours, but my hair is a nicer colour."

Natalie's joy burst out of her in peels of childish laughter at Micha's response. Not only did it prove beyond doubt that chimpanzees had the ability to recognise themselves and so had passed the so-called mirror test but it also showed that six million years of individual evolution had not stopped females from two different species being critical of what they saw in the mirror.

Natalie loved the time the two of them spent together sharing the mirror. She and Micha developed a routine of grooming and hair brushing that seemed entirely natural for them both. Sadly, mirrors had not always had such a positive influence on the troop.

When she was first developing the ape arena, Natalie had installed a shatterproof plastic mirror so she could indulge her curiosity about how the chimpanzees

175

would react to it. As if to test the credentials of the shatterproof object Sundance managed to rip it from the wall and smash it against the trees bending it hopelessly out of shape until he could manufacture a cutting edge that he used to threaten the keepers with. Natalie gave up on any further mirror experiments in the arena after that.

But before Sundance had weaponised the mirror, Natalie had seen him take a keen interest in it. She caught him more than once sitting, cross-legged in front of it, staring with a piercing intensity as if he was trying to carve his features into it through pure willpower alone. At other times when he thought no one was looking he would strut and pose in front of it, coming at it from either side and even from above as if he was trying to catch his reflection out. All these sessions ended with the same, inevitable, descent into a rage, though, as he charged the offending impostor that stood before him. Natalie was sure that a dark reason lay behind the attacks and was ashamed when she heard from Micha what drove them.

Natalie knew of Sundance's past experiences in the testing labs in Atlanta, and none of it made easy reading. He had been kept for years on a starvation diet, leaving him at almost half his normal body weight so that the scientists studying him could be sure that he would perform his tasks suitably motivated for his food rewards. He was subjected to an almost endless stream of studies to see how much punishment he would endure to gain some meagre handout.

Micha told Natalie that Sundance hated his reflection because he despised the ape he had been forced to become. The time in front of the mirror was an enforced punishment, a masochistic torture he used to stoke the fires that burned in him every day; to never let him forget what was taken from him by humans. Natalie wept as Micha told her of her father's despair. It was so clear to her that he was suffering terribly with post-traumatic stress disorder, but she could think of no way to reach him, to help guide him to a happier place.

When Natalie and Toby were not around, Micha had to re-enter a world that no matter how much she loved was becoming increasingly alien to her. The bond she had made with her human friends was driving a wedge between her and Sundance that pushed them further apart with every passing week. Micha tried to talk with them, to get them to see a world other than the pit of fury that Sundance had led them all into but she felt like she was losing the battle. When she felt safe enough to do so, she would bring up the topic of the humans, usually waiting until they had all eaten and Sundance was allowing himself to be groomed. She always started the chat on safe ground though.

"Tell us about the jungle Dad, tell us about home."

"Oh, that awful place," Sally would interject, just as keen to project her world view on them all as

Sundance was. "Full of snakes and bugs. You think you need grooming now; can you imagine how filthy you would be in that place? You'd be more nits than hairs."

It never mattered to Sally that she had been born in a zoo and spent her whole life in one and not once so much seeing a picture of the jungle; she had extreme views on the place, and none of them was positive.

If the mood took him, Sundance would reply, his words starting soft and low like distant thunder about to roll in across the plains; the threat of a greater ferocity to follow always present.

"The Great Green was our mother. It fed us; it protected us. During the day it kept the harsh sun off our heads, and at night it kept us warm, an endless blanket that took our bodies back into the soil when we had finished our time with them. Every animal in the Endless Tree knew the chimpanzees were in charge; we took what we needed, and our Eternal Mother never let us go without. We were never cold, even when the rains came and washed our beds away, the trees kept us dry, and the sun would warm us once more when the great clouds left, and the sky above us became an endless blue." His features would soften as his voice became more mournful, his early childhood memories reminding him of a time before the pain and rage.

"In the mornings I would climb to the highest tree and sit above the jungle and watch the sun rise over the great green, blue above me, green below with no way of seeing the edge of either. We did not usually go so high in the trees; we left the high branches to the lesser monkeys only going up there if we wanted them for a feast. But I loved it up there; it made me feel safe; until the day I saw the smoke, and the trucks and I knew the No Hairs had come."

Micha knew that every story would end up at this point and had to cut her father off before he took then down the inevitable path to a rage-fuelled rant.

"The jungle is still there, I have seen pictures of it, Natalie and Toby have shown me. Natalie has been there and seen the Chimpanzees that live there; our brothers and sisters that we have never met yet. Natalie says that many animals from zoos get taken back to the jungles, so they can live in the wild again. That might be us; we might get back there; you can sit in that tree again and watch the sunrise, I promise you, Papa; we can do this. The more I talk to them the more I can hear about it and the more I can make them want to take us back there."

"Who wants to go to that smelly place?" Sally would say. Usually, Micha's wild-born grandma, Savannah would step in at this point, perhaps sensing that she needed to speak before Sundance could.

"Maybe the child is right; maybe she can lead us back to our mother's arms. She has a gift, and I say she needs to keep using it. My daughter knows nothing of the Great Green. She has never tasted the cool, sweet air of a jungle morning after the rains in the night or feasted on colobus and papaya plucked from the trees that very day. She has never made her bed between the roots so mighty they make these walls seem like shrubs. She has never lain there and tried to count the numberless stars that shine through the leaves of the vast and endless canopy above us."

Savannah never liked to miss an opportunity to remind her daughter Sally about her wild born past and used it as constant means of keeping her place, high in the pecking order, much closer to Sundance than her age and gender would generally allow. At times like this, she could counsel Sundance, calming him to a point where he would dare to let himself dream of seeing the jungle once more. He would let the love and pride he felt for his incredible daughter overrule the fear her gift caused him. He would allow these feelings to dampen, if only for a moment, the furnace of hate that scorched inside him every day. In these rare moments of calm, Sundance knew that his only chance of ever seeing his home again rested with letting Micha continue her friendship with the two No Hairs, no matter how much that went against a lifetime of battling thoughts of murderous revenge.

After these sessions with his family, Sundance, would head to his high perch at the back of the arena, trying to regain a sense of how it felt to sit above the jungle. Occasionally, if he closed his eyes, he could recapture that sense of floating above it all that made him feel so free in his childhood home. It was in one of these moments that Micha finally picked up the courage to join her father on the perch, nestling in beneath his oak trunk arms and resting her head on his colossal chest.

"I love you, Papa. I know I have never suffered even for one day as you have done. I know that I have never seen the horrors that you have seen, but I ache with sadness every day when I see what it has done to you. I want to end your pain Papa; I want to set you free. Let me speak with the No Hairs, make them do what we want. I can do this; I know I can. But not if you fight me or if you scare them away. Let me tell them of your pain, make them see what they must do."

She didn't look up at her father when she spoke, fearful that even a glance of eye contact might be enough to wake the rage again. If she had, she would have seen two pools of tears filling Sundance's deep sockets, gullies of sorrow running between the mountainous outlines of his cheeks and weary brow.

"Take me home my Warrior Princess, take me home."

Chapter 23
Toby's Birthday Wish

Toby's twelfth birthday was July 23rd, a month to the day since his mother had died.

He had been dreading the day for weeks now, burying himself in the desperate hope that everyone would forget it and let the day slip by unnoticed.

On the morning of his birthday, Toby still did not know what he wanted to do. He was very clear on what he did not want — no surprise party, no friends from London to come down and stay, no big presents; but he had no idea what he did want. In the end it was his mum who decided for him.

Toby's Dad entered his bedroom where he lay, still unwilling to start the day.

"Toby, mate, I've got to give you something; it's a birthday card. It's from your mum."

Toby sat bolt upright.

"She wrote it a few weeks ago when she knew she would not be able to be here today. She asked me to get a little present for you as well, she was very persistent in what I had to get you, I guess it will mean something to you, but I have no idea why she was so desperate for me to get it."

Dan handed Toby the card, which was attached to a small parcel. He sat quietly, waiting for Toby to open it and read it before he said another word. Toby read the message it contained, to himself at first but then again out loud, his voice stretched and disjointed as he struggled to keep his emotions from hijacking the moment.

'Dear Toby, my beautiful boy. I am so sorry that I could not be with you today; I tried my very best to win this last battle, but it was not to be. I so wanted to be with you as you start this next amazing stage of your life, in your new home and a new school but please know that I will be watching over you and will be by your side when you need me most. Just listen quietly, and you will hear my voice. I will be there to guide you even though you will not see me; I will be in your heart always, as you are in mine. Your life will be an amazing journey. Try and make every day a day worth living. Learn something new every day, try something different every day, show love and kindness to everyone you meet and never waste a single day on hate, anger or regret. You have a charmed life ahead of you, Toby, use it for good. Do something incredible with it. You have an amazing dad who will catch you every time you fall, and you have an uncle who will run through brick walls for you so don't let a fear of the unknown hold you back. Be brave,

be bold, be brilliant. With your father's ambition, your uncle's brains and my love you can change the world if you want to Toby. Work hard, dream harder and love hardest of all. Keep your eye on the bigger picture but never forget about the little dots that make it up. Fill every moment with joy and adventure, Toby. Never stop exploring, never allow boredom to rob you of any opportunities and never let prejudice stop you from taking the road less travelled. Listen to those around you some of the time but listen to your heart all of the time. I loved you from the first moment I could feel you in my tummy, and I will never stop loving you, Toby. You are my beautiful boy, and you always will be. All of my love, always, Mum xxx'

When Toby looked up from the card, he saw his dad's face beaming with pride, tears of joy mingled with tears of sadness as they meandered across his cheeks. He hugged Toby silently, knowing that words would only serve to pollute the moment, like plastic bags on a pristine beach. Toby held the card flat against his dad's back eager to protect it from their tears and save it from being crushed by the weight of their feelings.

When the hug had run its course, Dan spoke first.

"God what a woman; we are going to miss her everyday Toby, but at least we will never forget her. You and me are gonna have some tough times between us over the next few years, but so long as we remember what your mum was like and just think what she would have done, we'll be all right. Now here, open your present, although god knows what you're gonna do with it."

The present was in a beautifully wrapped box not much bigger than the palm of his hand. Inside was a leather case containing an old, explorer's brass compass, the type that opened up to show the needle and dial inside. On the outside, it said, 'Toby Potter, 24. 07. 1999' and on the inside, it said, 'Plot your path and follow your heart.'

Like his dad, Toby was confused by the present at first. Of course, he loved it; he had always loved things like this that you could play within your hands, something that you could study and learn about. He had had a pocket watch for his tenth birthday and the usual small boy gifts like magnifying glasses, magnets and pen knives; the stuff that all good parents buy in the hope of recapturing an imagined childhood of their own.

But it was clear to Toby that this was not some throwaway gift from a local toy shop. He moved the piece around in his hand, flipping it over and feeling the smooth metal and subtle contours of the engraving with his thumb as he did.

Dan had sat with interest as he watched his son ponder and play with his gift, heartbroken that this would be the last gift he would ever receive from his mum but relieved to see the intensity with which he was studying it and the impact it was having on him.

"I love it Dad, it is beautiful, but I don't know how to use it, can you show me?"

"Course I can, mate, give it to your old 'boy scout' dad."

The rest of the day was spent like two young boys as they headed out to explore the coast that was only a few miles from the park. Dan showed Toby how to plot courses and take bearings, as they worked their way up and down the nearby beach, looking for treasure, finding lost coves, planning adventures and forgetting about life for a few glorious hours. It was gone six o'clock by the time they pulled into the driveway of the park, and Toby was keen to get to Micha while Dan was keen to check the preparations for the surprise party that his son had so clearly said he didn't want.

Natalie greeted Toby with a birthday hug that made him feel uncomfortable and self-conscious yet warm and secure and vaguely aware of future feelings to women like only a twelve-year-old boy can feel. Natalie was keen to get to Micha, so she could wish Toby a happy birthday as well.

Their walk that evening had been a stroll to take in every animal they could, almost like a victory parade as Micha told them all about Toby's birthday. Del Boy and Rodney had taken to joining them on nearly all of their trips now and had spent most of the evening chanting "Happy Birthday" to a point where Toby was really looking forward to it not being his birthday.

Midway through the walk they reached the outdoor seating area around the cafe and were amazed to see it lit up with dozens of fairy lights, a birthday banner stretched between two trees and four of the central table decorated with party tablecloths.

Micha looked to them both with excitement, sensing that more treats were about to appear as Natalie stepped back from them both, a shrug of her shoulders revealing her guilty secret in being a part of this deceit. As Toby stood there with Micha's hand in his, Dan and Jack followed by his grandparents, and all of the keepers came out from the cafe singing "Happy Birthday" each holding a plate of food or drinks and a small selection of presents. Toby didn't hesitate in breaking into the broadest grin, hugging his uncle and dad, so grateful that they had ignored his wishes, delighted to be able to feel like a young boy, spoiled and happy on his birthday.

Once the party started to draw to a close, Jack and Dan sat either side of Toby, and he was able to show them both the compass, allowing Jack to see for the first time what his dying sister had bought for her son. Unlike Toby and Dan, he showed no confusion at present but broke instead into a grin of immediate recognition. He called his father, Toby's grandfather, over to show him the gift and explain the significance.

"The Jack you see before you, was not always such an upright member of society Toby, there was a time when he was a lost soul with no idea which direction to take. His mother bought him a compass just like this, and I showed him how to use it, taught him how to plot a path and find the way home. Do you still have it, Jack?"

"Are you kidding me? It's on my office desk; I look at it every day. Matter of fact..." Jack pulled a box from his pocket. "I was going to hand it on to Toby today, but now I don't have to. Clever Alice, she always knew what to do."

Jack took out his compass and showed him the engraving inside, saying the same words as Toby's."

"So Toby or Not Toby, where are you going to plot your path to?"

Toby did not need to think of his answer; the words were out before he could question them.

"South Jack, I want to go south. I want to take the animals with me, and I want you to help me. We need to set the animals free."

This time Jack just nodded. He didn't see it, but Micha squeezed Toby's hand when she heard these words — she knew her journey was beginning.

Chapter 24
Micha's Ark

Toby had another six weeks between his birthday and starting at his new school, and his daily routine never varied over this time.

He would spend every morning or evening with Micha and the time in between working a full shift as a keeper. His duties in the zoo were mainly at the business end of the animals, cleaning their dung, changing their straw, washing out pens and chopping up the daily food rations but he loved every minute of it.

Without a doubt, his favourite part of any day was when there was a chat about the relocation program that had been given its official start date the day after his birthday. Jack had known that he was never going to win an argument with Natalie over what was best for the chimpanzees, but he was surprised when Toby had told him that the tigers, Omar and Salma should be included in his plans, as should Achilles. Toby made a good argument for all the big cats pointing out that Omar and Salma had failed utterly to produce a cub in all the time they had been together, and Achilles was seemingly destined to stay eternally single unless they moved him out of Europe. Natalie had given Toby the contacts to chase up for the relocation of Omar and Salma back to the sanctuary in the Periyar Tiger Reserve, deep in the heart of India's Kerala National park where there was a vast enclosure for Omar to live semi-wild in and a new breeding program that would hopefully give Salma a better chance at parenthood.

Achilles was a little more of a problem as there were so few of his kind left in north Africa and the risk of poaching so high that a move back to the Atlas Mountains would be too risky to contemplate. Fortunately, Toby had read about an area in eastern Congo where lions had been spotted returning, decades after their last appearance. The enormous reserve there measured over a million square kilometres and was trying to re-establish some apex predators. Although Achilles was not indigenous to this area, he could be used to start a breeding program with the female lions in the region whose cubs could then be raised as jungle lions.

Toby had spent his time over the summer making bigger plans for the zoo and was keen to share them with his uncle.

"I've been thinking Jack, is there a zoo hospital? You know a centre that just deals with sick animals from zoos around the country? So, the animals come here until they are well and then move on again."

"Not really, not one specialist centre. It is a bit of a

problem as we have to shift animals all around the country to find different specialists. Why, do you have a plan?"

"Well, yeah, I do. If there are not so many animals here maybe we should turn this place into a hospital rather than a zoo. That way we can earn money from treating the animals rather than showing them to the paying guests. If you built a big centre and got your friends, who are vets to work here you could make this the best place in the world for sick zoo animals. I bet you would be on the telly if you did that, you'd be dead famous and the TV lot would pay so much we would not have to keep the animals on show. What do you think?"

"I think you need to start going to school Tobe of Tobe Hall; you are spending way too much time around this place; if you here any longer you will be running the joint."

Toby laughed as he ducked out of the way of one of Jack's mock punches, but he could tell that his suggestion had not gone completely ignored; there had been a spark of interest that he figured he could build on over the coming months.

Natalie loved the idea from the start and was sure that a hospital could and should be the future for the zoo. She was getting more and more involved in the planning of the first wave of relocations and was able to spend less and less time devoted to Micha. Her extra work had meant that Toby and Micha were left on their own more, which suited them just fine. Without Natalie around, they were able to speak far more freely to the animals, ready to learn who wanted to go, and who wanted to stay.

Many of the other animals around the park, to Micha's surprise and on occasion, ill-disguised disgust, did not share her enthusiasm for a return to the wild. The big cats, at least, did show some approval for the plan. Omar and Salma broke their lifetime ban on showing the slightest interest in any animal that they did not intend to eat and spoke to Micha when she told them.

"If you get us home Tree Rat, we will be pleased."

Maybe not the greatest example of gushing gratitude but Micha took it as a significant step forward in chimpanzee/tiger relationships.

Achilles was marginally more magnanimous in his praise.

"The wild!" he roared, his mouth a cavernous gaping chasm. "I will smell the plains of my fathers again, taste the blood of a fresh antelope kill, lie with my pride and see the sky that never ends."

Toby was really pleased to hear how excited Achilles was but thought he would leave out the news about him going to the jungles of central Africa rather than back to the plains of the north just yet. He hadn't forgotten the lion's offer to eat him when he and Micha had first spoken with Achilles, and he was not looking to give him any more reasons to want to do this.

Many of the animals that Toby and Micha visited were happy to greet her as a friend, and the young chimpanzee was quick to learn from any and all of them. In particular, she

had taken a great liking to the lemurs after she had first met them at the start of

the summer and made sure that every walk included a swing by the enclosure for a five or ten-minute catch up with her most distant of cousins.

Toby needed no persuasion of this as he loved spending time with them as well, their self-assured confidence and cheeky, inquisitive nature making them a favourite with all of the guests. The first time Micha and the lemurs met it was the first time members of the two species had come, together. They had never lived together in the wild and had not even met before in zoos, so neither knew what to make of the other. Perhaps inevitably it was the First Lady of the lemurs, Sophia, who spoke first.

"Welcome Micha, will you share some fruit with us."

The lemur spoke in the natural tongue of all animals, changing from her regular series of closed and open-mouthed clicks that all lemurs used to the lower rumbling sounds that Toby knew to be the interspecies language. Micha was welcomed as a female first and ape second.

"We have heard much about you Princess Micha; how you will set your family free. Is that why you have come here Micha? Have you come to set us free?"

"Don't you want to be free?"

"Do you think we are not free? Do you think these walls contain us? We are lemurs, spirits of the night; we are not

kept here by the Hairless Ones. We rest here in the day, so our spirits are free in the night. If these humans wish to serve us, we will let them. Come warm your belly in the sun with me, sit here and close your eyes. Let the sun take your spirit on its journey let it show you that true freedom is only possible when you escape the chains of your body and let your mind take flight."

If the sun was at the right angle and Sophia was in a generous mood it was not unusual to find her with Micha and Toby all in a row. They would be sat on the grass, soles of their feet together, knees pointing out with their wrists resting on them and their heads back, eyes closed in full yoga repose, soaking up the precious solar gift. Sophia and the rest of the group had no desire to have their bodies relocated back to Madagascar, as their spirits went there every night as it was.

Micha was sure she was going to miss the lemurs the most when she got back to the jungle, well maybe not quite as much as she would Toby and Natalie, but not far behind.

Chapter 25
School Begins

Toby had been off school for so long by the time September came around that it came as a violent and unexpected assault when his dad told him that term started in two days' time.

St Augustine's School was founded in 1666 shortly after The Great Plague ended and had been infecting adolescent males with its peculiar brand of education ever since. The school was only thirty minutes away by the bus that ran past the end of his drive. As Toby was to discover, getting a bus to St Augustine's put him in a minority of one as the only pupil in the history of its existence to get there by public transport.

From his first day there, Toby recognised that this was a school like no other.

It had seven hundred pupils whose parents must have accounted for maybe ten per cent of the world's wealth. Its motto was 'Quality not Quantity' but when it came to money it was clear that quantity had a quality all of its own. The majority of the pupils boarded at the school and flew in at the start of each term from every corner of the world. It had been a military academy for over two hundred years and held on to this aspect of its past by employing an ex-Army officer to shout at the entire school every morning for thirty minutes of parade practice before they moved into the classrooms where the teachers took over the shouting.

The pupils seemed to relish in their ability to simultaneously flaunt and deny their parents' wealth in equal measure. They loved to tell anyone who would listen how much of Gloucester their parents owned but in the same breath would bemoan their troubled existence as they had to scrape by on barely two phone upgrades a year.

During the week, the school began at eight a.m. and finished at six p.m. with six hours of lessons, two of games and thirty minutes of parade practice every day; on Saturdays, it was eight-thirty until two p.m. Toby was speechless when he found this out. He would need to leave before his morning time with Micha and be back after it in the evening. The only crumb of consolation that he could glean from any conversation about his timetable was when his dad told him that the terms were only ten weeks long meaning he would break up for Christmas on the first of December having had a two-week half term in October. As good as this news was to Toby it was galling to Dan.

"Always the way, the more you pay, the less you stay!" he moaned "For what I'm paying them a term you'd have thought they'd keep 'em all year round."

The two and half months of that first term crawled at a pace of time that is usually used to describe how long it takes for planets to form and stars to die.

Any school can be a brutal and unforgiving for a child who does not fit in, but the harsh, cold, stone slab interiors of the centuries-old halls and corridors of St Augustine's added a layer of cruel indifference that seemed almost malicious in intent. Toby was at his least unhappy when he was able to lose himself in the darkest recesses of the school library, reading whatever he could find on chimpanzees, the Congo Jungle and, as his guilty secret, the books of Jules Verne.

It was almost the end of his second month at St Augustine's before Toby made a friend. His growing sense of isolation and alienation at school was eased by the one room in the whole building that could set him free. The library offered him silence and solitude, but more importantly a level of invisibility that allowed him to disappear into the books with no one paying him a second glance.

Of course, he was not alone in this desire for nonexistence. Many twelve-year-old boys feel so lost that they cannot imagine a world that allows them to exist. Their escape from this thought is to read books with such intensity that they cannot tell where reality stops and the pages begin. Because all the boys who went to the library went there to hide it was easy for Toby not to notice Chenna Mbaeri. He was able to completely miss his future lifelong friend as he sat unnoticed, dissolving into the mahogany bookcases, blending with chameleon-like subterfuge into the leather-bound literature of the languages section, willing the world to pass him by.

Until that day, Toby had not ventured into the language section. He tended to stay in the geography and biology zones, but he had found the need for a book on the languages of Africa as he realised he had no idea what they spoke in the Congo. It was when he was looking for something to help him learn more about the subject that he stumbled into his friendship, tripping over and collapsing onto Chenna, who had somehow camouflaged himself as an empty chair.

"Sorry, sorry, I didn't see you there, mate," Toby mumbled his apology and added, as if by way of an explanation "I was looking for a book on the languages of the Congo."

"I don't think there is one, but if it helps, we mostly speak French or English at home or Swahili when we are out in the country."

Not since Micha first spoke to him had Toby been so surprised to hear words come out of someone's mouth.

"Oh my god, no way. You are from Congo?"

"No, I am from the one next door, the DCR, the Democratic Republic of Congo," Chenna delivered this title with a flourish as if he was writing it with a feather quill in the air. "Although I don't think Democratic means the same thing in that part of the world as it does elsewhere, at least that's what my father says. Why do you want to know about The Congo, do you have an essay to write?"

"No, I want to take my chimpanzees back there." This sentence probably made a lot more sense to Toby than it did to Chenna.

"You have a pet chimp?"

"Chimpanzee, they don't like being called chimp, and no they are not my pets. They live in our zoo, and we are relocating them and lots of other animals back there. We are setting them all free and turning the zoo into an exotic animal hospital instead. I'm going to be vet there with my Uncle Jack". Toby had not, until this very minute, realised that this is what he was going to do but all of a sudden it made perfect sense to him, as if someone had turned his life map the right way up and for the first time he could see where he was supposed to be going.

"Oh, I just realised who you are, you're Bus Boy."

"Bus Boy? Is that what people call me?" Toby had never stopped to think what other people might make of him. He was so used to trying not to exist that it never occurred to him that the rest of the school might think that he actually did.

"Yes, but not in a bad way. They say things like 'oh leave him alone, he's Bus Boy, he's supposed to be a bit mental.' They call me much worse things than that and they never try to leave me alone."

And so it was, in one of life's many little ironies, Chenna and Toby found their voice and the courage to use it in the one place where they were supposed to stay silent. As they were the only two in the room, they did not need to worry too much about

disturbing any other students on that day or the many hundreds that were to follow in their school life together.

Toby had not noticed that he had spent his summer months undergoing an impressive growth spurt. It had left him taller than most of his year but looking like a child who had borrowed his parents' limbs and was not yet able to control them properly.

Chenna, by contrast, would not have seemed out of place in the early years of primary school, having not undergone a significant growth since his ninth birthday. This fact alone was enough to single him out for cruel inspection by every other pupil in the school but added to this was his French Congolese accent and a wild, exuberant hairstyle that on some days could almost double his body volume. Sadly, Chenna was the perfect storm of bully fuel. He was a small, vulnerable, frightened boy when

Toby met him, a fact that Toby had to remind himself of in the years to come when his friend would tower of him, engulfing him in his building-sized shadow.

Chenna boarded at St Augustine's as his father, wanted his son to be educated in Europe: first in England and then in France. He was hopeful that the boarding school in England would make Chenna resilient while the university education in France would make him wise. His father, Dr Mbaeri, was the Minister for Health and lived with the rest of Chenna's family in Kinshasa, the capital of the DRC.

Toby and Chenna were soon known as the Bus Boys, Double Decker and Minibus, and were gradually left alone, deemed too insignificant and maybe just a little too unpredictable to be bothered with. Toby surprised himself when he asked Chenna to come and see the zoo for the first time, but by the end of that first term, it had become a regular Saturday night event. Chenna was given a forty-eight-hour pass into the care of Dan Potter each weekend and an extended one for the two-week half term when Dr Mbaeri thought the return flight home was more trouble than it was worth for his young son.

It was not long into these visits that Chenna proved invaluable to Jack who was in desperate need of a link to the government of DRC if he was to secure the necessary paperwork for the relocation project.

What would have taken six to nine months of almost daily emails and faxes was completed in one short call by Chenna to his father. The permits were granted and the 'WWW Zoo Relocation Program' was given a date for take-off before Jack would normally have had time to complete the first round of paperwork.

Chapter 26
Toby and Sundance

When the plan finally fell into place, it did so with a speed that caught everyone at the zoo by surprise.

Once Toby had got Chenna involved, the necessary visas, work permits, travel documents and quarantine arrangements were completed in under a week rather than the year that Jack had anticipated. Chenna's father had been able to use his position in government to cut through bureaucracy denser than the jungle they were hoping to get to.

Toby had read all he could on the DCR and had chatted endlessly with Chenna about his homeland. It was clear from everything that he had heard that it could be a dangerous land where human life was worth very little and animal life almost nothing at all. It was by all accounts one of the most beautiful places on earth and also one of the richest. Sadly, as Jack was keen on saying, a jungle is worth nothing when it is living. Humans attach almost no value to a tree when it is alive and standing majestic, alongside equally magnificent towers of natural splendour. But cut it down and saw it into planks or burn it and plant a cash crop where it used to be, and you have a commodity worth selling. The Congo jungle lay like a beautiful green carpet on top of the richest mineral reserves in the world, and it was only the ravages of war that was stopping the people of the DCR from tearing up the floorboards to get at the treasures that were buried beneath their majestic home.

Toby knew in his heart that an animal as unique and splendid as Micha could never remain behind bars as an exhibit for the occasional bored passer-by to pull faces at. She needed to be in the wild. She had to get back to her spiritual home where she could become the Warrior Princess, she always knew she would one day be. They had spent so long together that Toby had stopped thinking of her as a talking chimpanzee and saw her just as Micha, his amazing, beautiful friend.

Despite their closeness, however, he was certainly not prepared for what Micha told him on one of their morning walks.

"My dad wants to speak to you."

Toby's mind went straight to red alert when these words trespassed across his mind. He had not forgotten the volcanic rage that had nearly engulfed him the first time they had met and nothing that had happened since then had made him think that Sundance's mood had cooled any.

"I think I should just send him a text, maybe from another country."

Micha had turned to face Toby, needing to see his

face to understand if he was serious or if he was trying to be funny, sarcasm generally being lost on her.

"You are right to fear him, but he has said he wants to talk so you will be safe. Anyway, you will be behind bars so what is the worst that can happen?"

Toby knew she was right. If he stayed behind the fence in the enclosure, the worst he would have to fear would be a well-aimed shot by Kianza with one of his disgusting pooballs, but Toby had decided in that instant that he was not going to stay behind the barrier.

The meeting with Sundance came about without any real planning; it was just an opportunity that presented itself. Natalie had become more and more relaxed with the rule about Toby and Micha being alone together and had let Toby put Micha away on his own more than once before, relying on the fact that she could use the code to open the inner door while Toby remained at that outer one. It was on one of these evenings when Toby and Micha were alone in the enclosure that Sundance came inside, on his own and sat by the door waiting for Micha to come back into her chimpanzee world. It was clear from the way that he was staring at Toby that he had chosen now as the time to talk.

Toby was taken by surprise by the sight of Sundance sitting in sombre anticipation but was not as scared as he had expected to be. Micha looked between them both and sensed that they were equally ready for this meeting to take place. She had expected Toby to wait outside the fence until she was back inside before beginning his chat with her dad so was unprepared for him to follow him into the enclosure, letting the outer door close behind him. Once that door was locked, he would need to use the code and a key to let himself out of both doors, there was no way he would be able to do this if Sundance was attacking him. She knew that by coming inside the enclosure, Toby was breaking the number one rule that Natalie had set and he was putting himself entirely at the mercy of Sundance's mood which was never a safe place to be.

The door clicked shut behind them, a cold metal warning to Toby that his last chance of escape had just sealed shut behind him.

"You wanted to talk to Toby, Father, well here his is."

She sat by her father, his frame dwarfing hers, a menacing shadow cast across her as the sun invaded the indoor arena, trying in vain to bring warmth to this frozen encounter. Sundance turned to face Micha for the first time since they entered the enclosure and barked a short series of low tone grunts that sounded like orders no matter what language they were spoken in.

"My father wants to know why you have come inside his home."

"Please tell him I did not want to be rude, I just wanted to sit next to him, man to man."

Micha replied to her father in their chimpanzee language. Sundance snorted at the end of what she said, finding the idea that Toby considered himself a male of equal stature to himself all the proof that he needed, that humans were all dangerously insane. The conversation continued as a series of interpreted messages that Micha did her best to translate with sufficient politeness and deference to keep Sundance seated and calm and with enough insults removed to keep Toby from walking out and calling off the whole relocation altogether.

"Why should we trust you No Hair child, every bad thing that has happened in my life has come from humans. My family murdered, my life of torture and now captured behind these bars. What did we ever do to you to deserve this?"

"I'm so sorry for everything that has happened to you but that wasn't me, it wasn't my dad or Jack or Natalie. They all want you to be happy again, none of us wants to cause you any more pain. I promise."

Many of the words did not translate exactly into chimpanzee, but it was evident from Toby's humbled expression that he was honest in his apology and Sundance, although he would never say it, respected the fact that he had come into the enclosure with Micha rather than sticking to the refuge of the outer section. Most of all though, he had learned to trust his daughter, and she was sure that Toby was speaking truthfully when he said that he wanted what was best for the troop, was sincere in his belief that he could get them back to the jungle that he so desperately wanted to see again before he died. But a lifetime of brutality at the hands of the No Hairs could not be quickly forgotten or ever forgiven.

"No Hairs are all alike. You kill for fun; you take more than you need, you burn what you don't want, destroy what does not belong to you. You think you are the only thing that matters. You will kill all that lives until all that is left is you, then you will kill yourselves."

"I think you are right about many humans, but not all of us. We want to protect you and the world you live in."

Toby knew it was a mistake as soon as he said that Sundance needed protection. Micha had translated it as keeping safe, which in the chimpanzee world is the role of the Alpha Male, which somehow made it worse.

"You think I need you to keep me safe? From what?" Sundance had stayed seated still but was shifting from side to side more now, and his shoulders had arched back, and his hair was puffed up, needlessly making him appear even more imposing. Instinctively Toby lowered his head and gaze and shook from side to side as if his whole body was disagreeing with what had been said.

"Sorry, no, no that is not what I meant. We want to preserve your way of life, protect the jungle, let you be free, away from humans. That is what we are planning for you. We are getting ready to leave very soon, the flights have been arranged."

Sundance seemed to be calmed by these words.

He was ready to continue the talk, learn more of Toby's plans but Kianza entered the enclosure before anyone got a chance to speak again. The young male chimpanzee did not hesitate when he saw Toby on his side of the fence, he let out a high-pitched screech that echoed around the chamber and set out on a low four-legged charge at Toby, his head down but gaze up under his thick, bulbous brow, his yellow eyes on fire with hate. Micha sprang to her feet to protect Toby, standing tall on her hind legs and waving her arms high above her head, matching Kianza screech for screech in a deafening crescendo of calls. She ran to meet Kianza as he charged. In between each shriek she called out, "Run Toby, run" pleading him to get to the door.

Kianza met Micha with his shoulder driving deep into her exposed tummy, a sickening thud as he knocked her off her feet and slammed her into the concrete floor. He did not waste time trying to inflict more damage on her but was slowed momentarily by her efforts to grab hold of his legs and pull him to the ground. The delay gave Toby enough time to get to the inner door, but he was struggling to enter the code, his terror turning his hands to ice.

Kianza had broken free from Micha's grip and was continuing his charge, mouth gaping open to reveal ferocious canines that would inflict terrible damage on Toby in seconds. Micha was calling out to Toby, "Quickly, quickly, run Toby run," but it was clear he was going to lose the race, and Kianza was two bounds away from unleashing those battering ram fists and knife-like teeth on him. Toby gave up all hope of escape and turned to cower in the corner by the gate, burying his head and turning his back to the oncoming fury in a hopeless attempt to lessen the assault.

But Kianza never finished his charge; Sundance had waited to the last second to time his attack when Kianza was airborne in his final stride. The alpha male used every ounce of his phenomenal strength to catch the younger male in mid-air and hurl him to the ground, a few feet from where Toby was huddled. As Kianza hit, the floor Sundance leapt on him, his arms a whirlwind of flailing fists that unleashed a thunderstorm of blows on the young ape. The angry, warrior screams that had started the charge had now turned to yelps of pain and confusion as Kianza saw his supposed ally in this attack turn traitor on him. Sundance was bellowing colossal roars of anger as he held Kianza down, allowing Toby the chance to escape unhurt from the enclosure.

The next day when Micha joined Toby and Natalie for her morning stroll, she relayed a little to Toby about what Sundance had been saying to Kianza during the fight.

"If you come near this human again, I will squash

you through the fence and feed what is left of you to the rats. Do you hear me, child? Nothing will put at risk our return to the wild, nothing and no one."

There had been so much menace in those words that everyone in the troop knew they applied equally to them all. They knew as well that there would be no more discussion about whether they were going or not.

Chapter 27
Pack your Bags

As much as it had never occurred to the adults that Toby would be joining them on their journey to the Congo, it had never occurred to Toby that he wouldn't be.

When the news came through that a date for the relocation had been agreed, Toby was hit with a wave of euphoria that turned to a crushing dread the moment he digested the news fully. The most important person in his life was about to begin a journey that would end with him never seeing her again.

Jack had broken the news to Toby, Natalie and Dan over dinner in the cottage. It was a Saturday night which meant that it was takeaway night and as usual Chenna had joined them for his weekend release from his school interment.

"Oh, by the way, I had confirmation today; all the papers are cleared, and the transport has been booked, we are cleared to go the first week in December, with any luck we will be back by Christmas."

Jack had delivered his news like he was mentioning, in passing, that his car had passed its MOT. The words took a second to sink in before everyone whooped and hollered for joy and Jack could crack an enormous grin. Natalie leapt up and hugged him, and Dan applauded them both.

"We couldn't have done it without Chenna, that's for sure, thank you so much for all of your help. We are cleared to take Sundance, Kianza, Micha, Sally, Daphne and Cindy. Butch will stay behind, and no doubt take the alpha spot, and Fredo and Sonny are going to move to a Dutch zoo for a breeding program that will see them back in the wild hopefully in eighteen months' time. Oh, and Achilles is going on the same flight but will be moved to a different reserve to the west of the chimpanzee area, further downstream where the Apex Predator Project is being run; his brides await him, lucky fella."

"That's great timing; I won't have to miss any school cos I'll have broken up by then."

Toby's words did not get the response he was after.

"You're not going." Dan, Natalie and Jack chimed in perfect harmony.

Dan's next words were not well planned.

"If you think that I'm going to let my only son, go and get killed in that godforsaken, disease-ridden shit ho…" It dawned on him mid-way through his rant that he was sat next to Chenna, son of a government minister and resident of DRC from birth.

"Sorry, Chenna, I know it's your home, but that place scares the hell out of me."

Dan spoke with the plea of a man wanting to be understood as someone who was just thinking of others.

"It is quite all right Mr Potter I understand that my home is a mystery to all of you." Chenna's formal speech reflected the mind of a child picking one of the three languages that he regularly spoke in.

He smiled through every word that he spoke, his impossibly generous nature forgiving everyone their ignorance of his home, his life, his struggles.

"You are right to fear some parts of my country, it can be very dangerous in certain areas, but these are far away from the cities that you are talking about and even from the reserves which are in the protected areas of the jungle. My father is working with the government to fight many of the bad men who try to take power and is helping to provide health care to the very poorest. If we can make their lives better, then they will be able to escape from poverty and become a more valuable part of our society."

The last part certainly sounded like a rehearsed bit of speech by his dad that Chenna had picked up, but everyone could see the sincerity in his eyes as he spoke about his homeland.

"My father is working so hard to make these areas better for everyone who lives there; you will see how much he has done. He does not want to build big hospitals that no one can afford to visit as the last Health Minister did, he wants to get cheap medicines, trained nurses, midwives and clean water to the villages so that they can help themselves where they are and not have to walk a hundred miles to the nearest clinic. The improvements are already happening, and it is great to see. I am very excited to go back and see what more he has done. When I am your age Mr Potter, I believe that my country will be the most successful in Africa, maybe you will all want to emigrate there rather than the other way round." Chenna finished with an even bigger smile than he started with, grateful that he got a chance to speak of the father he was so proud of.

"It will be an honour to meet your father Chenna; he sounds like an amazing man and you are an incredible boy; it is an honour to know you," Jack placed his dinner plate sized hand on Chenna's shoulder and gave him a gentle shake that must have felt like an earthquake to the tiny lad.

"You will be so very welcome, all of you. My country is the most beautiful in the world. The drive from Kisangani and then the boat ride up the Uele River, cannot be explained in words; you will think you have gone back in time, maybe expect to see a dinosaur walk past."

"Natalie and I have both been there before, a few years ago, and you're right, it is like the birthplace of the world, you cannot imagine that jungle like that still exists, as it did two million years ago. It has areas the size of France that has never been explored, imagine what might still be living in there." Jack turned to Toby as he spoke, too excited to remember that he was supposed to be putting his nephew off going.

"When I spoke with my father today, he was very excited at meeting you all and helping with your project. He has promised us a full escort at all times and has personally ensured that the passage from Kisangani to the reserve will be under his full protection. He and I hope very much to join you if you will permit it, we both want to see your chimpanzees make it to their new home."

"Daaaaad!" Toby managed to fit five extra syllables into that word, the full injustice of his plight could not be expressed in any fewer. "There is no way Chenna can go on this trip and I can't, that is so unfair."

Dan could see he was in a tricky spot here so pressed the parental escape button.

"We'll see son; I need to think about this."

Dinner finished in relative silence after this, everyone wanting to talk more about the trip but no one wishing to make Toby feel worse about the prospect of not going.

Toby and Chenna left the adults and went for a walk around the park, taking in, as they always did, a detour past the chimpanzee arena. Micha was sat by the glass wall, hoping Toby would take his usual evening route. Their interaction was the briefest of eye contacts, and their palms pressed either side of the glass divide but it was enough to reassure each other that everything was still OK. Sundance was sat a little way behind his daughter and watched the two as they shared this momentary contact. Toby looked at her mighty father and for once did not see murderous rage staring back at him, for once he saw what looked a little like trust. Maybe, if he squinted.

"I will ask my father to speak to your dad and invite you to come with me for the holiday if you would like, I am sure he will agree once he hears what my dad has prepared for us."

"Can he do it quickly, we've only a few weeks of term left."

As it turned out Toby need not have worried; Chenna set up a Facetime with his father the next day, and Mr Potter and Dr Mbaeri were able to speak face to face about the Christmas relocation, with Jack and Natalie sat to the side, off camera, listening to every word the minister had to say.

Dr Mbaeri was an enormous man, as tall as Jack but twice as wide. It was a struggle to fit his head on to the iPad screen they were using to talk. He spoke at least as much with his hands as his mouth and rarely managed to stay sat down; such was his excitement and energy. He smiled through every word, just like his son, his grin threatening to slice off the top of his head at any time; the gaps between his teeth showing that there was room for another set in there at least. His laugh boomed like a ship's cannon and sounded the end of each sentence, letting everyone know just how happy he was with the words he had chosen.

By the end of the call, Toby knew he would need his suitcase down from the loft; there was no way his dad was going to say no now.

Chapter 28
The Crate Escape

The rules governing flying animals around the world are every bit as strict as the ones for humans, even more so when you allow for all the vaccinations and quarantine laws that need obeying.

Transporting live exotic animals is strictly controlled, and the law says that they have to each travel in a crate that is strong enough to contain them but big enough to let them stand and move around in. They must be adequately ventilated but not allow fingers to poke in or out of them and they must contain enough bedding material for the animal to sleep as usual. This meant that between them they had had to get half a dozen chimpanzee proof crates and one lion resistant ones as well.

None of this was cheap, and Dan was never slow in letting them know how much they were all costing him. Of course, the zoo had been quick to publicise their adventure to the Congo and had organised many events for the public to come and say goodbye to the chimpanzees and Achilles. The guests were also able to get a look at the plans for the new hospital that was being funded partly by their donations and partly by a surprisingly large government grant that Jack had been able to secure through contacts at the International Development Fund that were sponsoring links with the DRC.

As Toby had predicted, the TV channels were very interested in the idea of a hospital for sick animals and two producers from Channel 4 had been down already, both noticing how great Jack and Natalie would look on the telly.

When Jack and Natalie weren't posing for the cameras, they were trying to organise transport for almost one and a half tonnes of crates and live animals to Gatwick, North Terminal where the freight services were available to fly them direct to the DRC Capital, Kinshasa. It was not going to be the most comfortable flight for any of them, but the animals would at least be partially sedated for the trip. Unlike the humans who were going to be strapped into cargo seats with no in-flight entertainment and definitely no service from the trolley. It had been agreed, very quickly by the two boys, that Chenna and Toby should fly with a regular airline, travelling under the safety of diplomatic protection meaning that queues and delays evaporated in front of them as they were escorted through the airports and onto the plane, a member of the DRC embassy staff with them at all time.

Anyone who has tried to get a cat into a carry case

for a trip to the vets will know that the pet rarely enters into this arrangement eagerly. Multiply this problem up to the size of Achilles or the temperament of Sundance, and it was clear the challenges that Jack and Natalie faced.

In the end, it was Micha who won her father and the rest of her family over. She explained to them that there was no leaving the zoo and no chance of ever seeing the jungle again if they did not agree to get in the crates. She gave Natalie the idea of putting the crate that she was going to travel in into the enclosure so she could use it for a few nights, showing the rest of the troop how she could make a nest and sleep in it quite comfortably. As she hoped, the rest of the family succumbed to curiosity and jealousy and were fighting over it within two nights. Sundance did need quite a bit of persuasion from Micha, but eventually, he allowed all the crates to be brought in for the last two nights in the zoo, reluctantly agreeing to sleep in it for the last night so Natalie and Jack would be happy that he was ready to make the trip.

Micha and Toby had visited Achilles every day for the two weeks leading up to the trip, warning him that a crate would appear in his enclosure soon and explaining why it was there. For all his pompous preening and regal sense of entitlement Achilles had a practical understanding of what was needed to survive. His time in the wild had taught him that not every chase resulted in a kill and not every day was a good one; he saw the crate for what it was, a necessary injustice along the road to his eventual manumission. While he intended to give his keepers a tough time over it, he made it clear that he would be getting into the crate to ensure that he made his final journey back his beloved wild existence.

For the humans, Jack and Natalie were always going to make the journey as were Toby and Chenna which left one undecided member of the team. Dan left his decision right to the last forty-eight hours before take-off. In the end, the decision was easy for him. The wounds of losing his wife less than six months earlier were still too raw for him to contemplate being separated from his son for such a long time. So it was that Dan Potter, a man raised in a north London council tower block and who still, despite his vast fortune, considered foreign food to constitute anything not served with chips and ketchup was heading to the Democratic Republic of Cong: a country ranked on every level to be one of the poorest and least stable countries in the world. It was probably just as well that Dan never paid much attention to the news.

The journey time to the airport was two hours, the flight time to Kinshasa eleven hours and then the internal flight to Kisangani a further two hours. Add on the inevitable waiting time for the animals to be checked and the crates loaded on and off the freight aircraft, and the whole trip was expected to take twenty-four hours.

The guidelines recommend that two gallons of water per chimpanzee per twenty-four hours is required, with more needed for a lion. Add to this the food, medications, gloves, masks, aprons, baby monitors, thermometers, tools for the crates, ramps and trolleys, emergency batteries, veterinary inspection certificates, medical records, travel permits and just about anything else that wasn't nailed down in the zoo and it was clear just how much work Jack and Natalie had to do before the convoy could leave for the airport.

Micha had reassured Toby that all of the animals making the trip knew that it would take a whole day, and they would be in the crates for all this time, but obviously, he had no way of passing this on to Jack, who still knew nothing of her amazing talent. Sundance and Kianza were busting open with excitement at the thought of getting to the jungle and were ready and waiting by their crates on the day of the move. Daphne and Cindy were excited too but nervous at what might happen along the way. They both loved Sundance and would have followed him anywhere so were also ready to enter their crates when asked.

Sally, on the other hand, was literally clinging to her favourite tree in the arena and was screeching at the keepers when they came to get her. Natalie was unable to coax in her with treats, and no amount of promises and pleadings from Micha made any difference. In the end, Jack was forced to give Sally a chow ball laced with a sedative. That calmed her enough for him to give her an injection that knocked her out completely, so they were able to gently lay her in her crate, surrounded with treats, bedding and her favourite toys.

True to his word Achilles was going down swinging. He had every intention of getting in the crate but was giving the keepers plenty to remember him by. He had started pacing the perimeter of his arena from first light and was rocking from side to side, shaking his mane and pawing at imaginary threats every time any keeper came with into view. His roaring could be heard from every corner of the park, a continuous stream of threats, boasts and insults but all with an undercurrent of one word repeated again and again, "Freedom."

No keeper was willing to go near the enclosure when Achilles was acting like this.

When he occasionally stopped his menacing patrol of the enclosure, he would open his mouth to its full cavernous extent, a 120-degree gape that revealed an arsenal of lethal canines and incisors that threatened to shred anyone foolish enough to enter the compound.

Toby had been watching the show Achilles was putting on and could hear that Jack was planning to get the rifle, ready to dart him. Toby was getting worried that Achilles might get injured and not be able to make the trip but his roaring had not gone unheard by Micha who had expected this display and was ready for it.

She explained to her father that the trip was

dependent on all of them leaving together so the chimpanzees could not leave without Achilles. She told him that he was scared of the crate but would not admit it. Sundance was familiar with those feelings, but if his return to the jungle relied on Achilles getting in his container, then he was going to make it happen anyway he could. His torrent of barks, hoots and growls matched Achilles' roars in volume and menace and sent a loud, clear message, one alpha to another.

"If you get in your crate your next roars will echo around the planes and jungles of the wild. Your prey will hear it and fear you. Come brother let us begin this journey home."

Achilles was happy that his efforts had not gone unnoticed by the Tree Rats and was pleased that they had recognised how mighty his roar was. Just as Jack was loading the rifle, Achilles stopped his pacing, yawned and headed straight to his crate where he lay down and almost instantly fell asleep.

Each of the crates weighed almost two hundred kilogrammes when empty, once fully loaded they were nearer three to four hundred kilogrammes and represented a formidable challenge for the forklift driver and team when loading into the specially ventilated cargo lorry that was on hand to take them to the airport. Compared to the humans, however, the animals were going to have a comfortable ride. Natalie, Dan and Jack, were strapped into uncomfortable, folding chairs in a noisy lorry and then an aircraft with no windows, no cushions and no miniature bottles of wine and scotch to make the trip a little more bearable.

Undeterred Jack was gripped with childlike excitement about the trip and could not help hanging off the back of the lorry and shouting to the gathered keepers.

"Farewell fellow zookeepers and animal lovers, let our wild peripatetic peregrinations begin."

Del Boy and Rodney words were simpler and to the point but came more from the heart. For human ears, they chanted, in perfect Parrot speak, "Aaak Micha is leaving, bye, bye, Micha, Aaak."

For the animals, they made their feeling far more understandable.

"Our Queen is leaving. Long live Micha, long live the Queen. We love you, Micha."

Micha could hear the birds calling to her from their treetop perch and was touched by their words, even if she knew that they meant Queen of Gossip.

They did love Micha, but it was her gossip that they were really going to miss.

Chapter 29
Boots on the Ground

They have a saying in the Army that "a plan only lasts until the boots hit the ground".

Dan, who had never spent a day of his life in the armed forces was very fond of using this phrase as a way of showing his disbelief in anyone's ideas but his own.

Despite Dan's worst predictions and the incredibly complex travel plans of six chimpanzees, one lion, three adults and two children the flight to Kinshasa went without a hitch as did the connection to Kisangani. The chimpanzees were reassured continuously by Micha who kept up an endless flow of hoots, grunts and quiet rumbles that served to keep them all pacified to the point that not even Sundance required any further sedatives for the whole of the journey. For her part Natalie kept a running commentary going for Micha, her usual unanswered stream of questions, anecdotes and titbits kept Micha completely up to date about how the trip was going while leaving no one listening in any the wiser about how valuable the conversation was to the brilliant young ape.

This smooth transition would certainly not have been the case if they had not had the assistance of a high-ranking government official, their personal Army escort and a private cargo plane laid on by Dr Mbaeri, as a welcome present from the Government of the DRC, for the internal flight to Kisangani. It was from here that the overland trek to the Sanctuary would begin.

The chimpanzee sanctuary where they were heading was north of Bondo in the Bidi region, famous for the enormous chimpanzees and their vast colonies. The sanctuary was run with the help of the government and the United Nations and was seen as an effort to help the region become more stable and allow much-needed infrastructure to be built for some of the poorest people in Africa. It was this aspect that interested Dr Mbaeri as he knew that overseas funds could be used to save both the animals and the humans of the region if they were used in the right way; he was happy to help the chimpanzees only in so much as they were able to help his people.

From the moment they met, it was apparent that Jack and Dr Mbaeri were going to be friends. For Jack, the meeting offered him that very rare feeling of not being the biggest guy in the room and also, maybe not even the smartest. Dr Mbaeri's stature was hard to take in at first sight. He made no apology for his size and wore his physicality as a shield and badge of honour, using it to establish a natural pecking order within any group that he found himself in. Once this was determined, however, he was kind, thoughtful, polite and endlessly charming to all that he met.

The minister had greeted them at the airport and had made it clear from his opening boom of a laugh that he was the Top Dog; it was his show, and he was in charge. He engulfed his son, throwing him around like driftwood on a stormy sea.

Chenna was used to this elaborate and athletic display of affection but had begun to feel that at thirteen it was maybe a little embarrassing. He made an effort to hide these feelings, of course, and wrapped his arms around his father's head as if it was a regularly sized waist he was hugging.

Once the Mbaeri's had finished their embraces, Dr Mbaeri turned his attention to the tired and fraught looking band that had joined his son on his journey home. He threw wide his arms as if attempting to hug them all at once, a feat he could easily have managed, and bellowed out a welcome, so over the top and so enthusiastic that it was impossible for them all not to bask in the warm glow it cast over them.

"Mes amis, bienvenue à La République Démocratique à Congo. Welcome, my friends, welcome. We must get you and your most precious cargo on the next stage of this epic journey, but first, you must rest, wash, eat; let us make you feel human again after your long flight. Dan Potter, Jack Friday and

Natalie Brooker, you have spent too long with the chimpanzees; come to spend some time with us primates instead."

The minister shook each of them by hand as he said their name, a flawless example of a man at the peak of his powers working the crowd to perfection. He spoke as if surrounded by cameras, the producer, director and star of his own personal reality TV show.

As tempting as a hot shower and good meal sounded to Jack and Natalie, they were both keen to keep the time in the travel crates as short as possible for their animal entourage, so both requested as politely as possible that they continued to Kisangani as quickly as possible. The minister made no show of his slight disappointment at the alteration to his carefully rehearsed script and assured them that they would be back in the air within the hour a fact that horrified a very tired and hungry Dan every bit as much as it delighted Jack and Natalie.

The cargo plane organised for the internal transfer to the north east of the country was a converted jumbo jet that was often used in times of crisis to move reserves of medicines and medical teams to areas of need. The space at the back was more than sufficient for the crates, and the seats at the front were the remnants of business class making them fare more comfortable than anything the travellers had experienced on the trip so far. Dan was delighted to see that Dr Mbaeri had laid on food for the journey. As he always did, the big man made the mistake of assuming that everyone would eat at least as much as he did, the children included. There was enough to feed them for a week, rather than the two-hour flight that separated the two cities.

Toby had been very quiet since landing at Kinshasa. The flight with Chenna had been great fun, a film and snacks binge with the diplomatic envoy leaving them very much to themselves. But from the moment he stepped off the plane he had been battered by an assault of sights, sounds and smells that left him reeling. From the hair dryer blast of heat as the plane doors opened to the wall of humanity that was Chenna's father Toby was reeling from the moment his feet touched the ground.

By the time he made it onto the transport plane, the adults were deep in conversation. To his amazement and deep concern, it was his dad and Dr Mbaeri who were leading the debate. Toby did not trust Dan to keep the worst extremes of his political views entirely to himself during a conversation like this; Chenna was looking on and judging by his expression shared Toby's concerns.

The flight was taking them across the centre of the DRC, and a vast green carpet lay beneath them. It was crisscrossed by what looked like huge rivers but were, in fact, minor tributaries to the mighty River Congo, an almost three thousand-mile-long river that reaches ten miles wide in parts and is over two hundred metres deep at its deepest, feeding a rain forest larger than the whole of western Europe. From the plane, it was possible to see the pockmarks of human development within the forest, ugly scars left by mines, roads and burning deforestation. Towns sprawled out into the jungle, their edges hidden by the canopy, as though they were an invading parasite crawling under the skin of nature's most beautiful creation.

Dan was sat in a window seat, staring out at the endless panoply of nature's achievements below. He could not hide his awe at the majesty of what was being revealed beneath him, even if his words didn't quite do it justice.

"Jeez Louise, that's a lot of trees."

Dr Mbaeri laughed from the depths of his belly, the vibrations rocking his chair and the hoots of joy drowning out the engine noise.

"You are right, Mr Potter, that is a lot of trees. But it is so much more. It is the richest, most diverse natural ecosystem in Africa. Contained beneath are the richest mineral reserves in the world and running through it is the second largest river in the world. My country is bigger than Europe, but it has a population only slightly bigger than your country alone. Eighty million people live here but less than one quarter live in the big cities. The other sixty million live in the areas you see below, spread out along the thousands of miles of riverbanks most of them living their whole lives within a few miles of where they were born. Over two hundred and fifty different ethnic groups exist in the DRC. That is more groups than there are countries in the world, Mr Potter. Our population is more diverse than the United Nations!" Dr Mbaeri threw his arms wide as if he was surprised by his facts, amazed at the expanse of the country he was describing.

"All those resources down there, all that untapped wealth and yet your country is so raggedy arse poor. Why is that? 'Ow can you be so rich and so broke at the same time? It don't make sense; there must be a reason."

By Dan's standards, this was a polite, dinner time, observation. One that might not even have warranted a kick under the table from Alice had she been around.

"Do you think there is just one reason Mr Potter, just one simple solution that will explain everything?"

Dr Mbaeri's questions were given without expectation of reply or with any malice, but they were intended to make the listener think.

"My beautiful country down there cannot exist without a strong government, but the strongest government in the world cannot be expected to provide one single solution that fixes all the problems. Perhaps in time, with us all working together we can chip away, case-by-case until we build a better, richer, healthier society for our children to grow in. Who knows? Maybe when our great-grandchildren are looking for schools, it will be the young Potter who comes to Kinshasa to study, not the other way round!"

Again, Dr Mbaeri finished his sentence with a loud bark of a laugh and punch of the air with his head-sized fists.

"You believe that? You think your country, or the rest of Africa will ever change? You've had people living here longer than any place on earth, and you've got more resources than Europe ever had but we got rich and you got poor, nothing's ever gonna change that, just the way it is, just natural economics. "

Like many incredibly wealthy people, Dan assumed he had an innate and intimate knowledge of every aspect of global finance, despite never once having studied any part of it. By contrast, Dr Mbaeri was a genuine world authority on the subject.

"You are right Mr Potter, humans have lived down below us for longer than almost any place on earth, over ninety thousand years in fact."

If he had taken offence at Dan's comments, Dr Mbaeri did not show it for one second, his smile never flickering below both broad and beaming even once.

"Despite this, we are ranked in the bottom ten poorest countries in the world with two-thirds of the population living in extreme poverty. That is terrible isn't Mr Potter? Two-thirds of my people living in such poverty that they will not eat every day or have clean water. People who earn less than a dollar a day so can never save enough to change their circumstances on their own. You are right this has been the case for centuries. But did you know that two hundred years ago over eight percent of people in the world lived like this? That's right Mr Potter every country in the world used to live like we do but almost every single one has worked their way out of it. Do you think that we in Africa and here in the DRC, are so special and so different that we can't do what every other country in the world had done? Do you think that is so Mr Potter? Or do you not think it was maybe that we were the most abused, so we are the last to recover?"

Even when discussing such a terrible topic his smile never left his lips; the words that he was saying were a source of inspiration and hope, not despair and recrimination.

"Don't worry, sir, I am not about to blame our colonial past, and if I did it would be Belgium, not Britain I would be blaming. I am Minister of Health in this government; I am supposed to heal the sick. But I will not do it by building them grand hospitals that none of them can get to, or afford when they get there. I will do it by getting them roads, and water, and electricity and nurses and midwives in their villages and keeping their children in school. That is how we will lessen sickness and ease poverty, one trained nurse at a time. That is how I will do it, what do you say to that, Mr Potter?"

Dr Mbaeri sat back in his chair and took along drink from his chilled water bottle, a satisfied grin on his face, the look of a man who knew what the world wanted of him, confident that he could deliver it all.

Dan sat in silence, unable to form any answer, stunned by the passion and intensity of the mountainous man sat next to him. Fortunately, the captain broke the silence by announcing that they would be coming into land in a few minutes, warning them that it might be a little bumpy. As the plane was one of the Congo Airways fleet, an airline that is banned from flying into almost every country in the world due to safety concerns, this did not fill any of them with confidence.

As it happened, the landing and unloading of the cargo went without a hitch. It took a few more days of having boots on the ground before the plan started to unravel, in a frighteningly and fatal manner.

Chapter 30
Forest Grump

After the plane had landed at Kisangani, the crates were loaded onto transporter trucks that had been provided by the Army, which had a large garrison on the outskirts of the city.

Without ministerial support, this stage would have been fraught with danger and incredibly difficult to arrange. With Dr Mbaeri's presence, however, the colonel from the garrison, himself, had overseen every aspect of the transition from plane to boat to camp and had sent a company of a hundred soldiers under the command of his most trusted captain.

The flight to Kisangani had taken less than three hours but seemed to have flown them back to the beginning of time. Not the city itself, which was busy and modern and chaotic and loud but the reserve which was a further half day's journey by boat upstream.

The Maringa Reserve is on the south bank of the Congo opposite the town of Bumba. The reserve covers an area half the size of England but has a single encampment on the shores of the river that houses all of the accommodation, the animal hospital, medical centre, research centre and administration buildings from which the whole site is managed.

The entire reserve is home to barely half a million people, mostly made up of the local indigenous population who have lived an unchanged existence for millennia but also many displaced people forced out of their homes from the surrounding areas by war, brutal militia and deadly poachers who plague the whole region.

The scientific centre at the heart of the village was founded by the African Wildlife Foundation and was funded through Central African Environmental programs that Dr Mbaeri was very excited about.

He was clear in his vision that lifting people out of extreme poverty and environmental protection were inexorably linked. If he wanted to protect the animals from the bushmeat trade and poachers, then he knew he had to offer alternatives that were more attractive to the local humans.

He knew that there could never be enough soldiers in all of DRC to secure these remote areas. But he hoped there might be enough teachers, nurses and midwives to educate and protect the residents long enough to allow a whole new generation of healthy, trained individuals to grow; ones who shared his values and wanted to secure their environment.

At the time of this first trip, however, there was no mistaking that there was still a long way to go.

For the first time in his life, Toby was confronted with mud streets and crumbling lean-to houses that seemed to have collapsed against each other like drunks at a bar holding each other up, but only just. The houses stretched down to and even into the river, stilts lifting them up and keeping them dry from the mighty waters flowing beneath them.

Electric cables hung from house to house in a haphazard sprawl, as if dropped from a plane by a neglectful pilot. Horse-drawn carts vied for position in the mud ruts, competing with goats and dogs that wandered the streets untethered.

The heat seemed to have risen two or three degrees from the city, and the air lay still, clinging to the streets, trapping the smells of the river and the clawing stench of the fish market leaving all of the visitors reaching for handkerchiefs and bandannas to position, however subtly, over their noses. Toby stood and stared, unable to focus on any single, particular item that confronted him, his senses stretched beyond coping by the assault of so many previously unseen, unheard, unsmelled, and untasted sensations.

Instinctively Chenna put his arm around his friend's shoulder. "I know how alien this can all look when you see it for the first time, but don't worry this is not so very different from where I grew up or how much of my family still live." Chenna was proud of his upbringing and did not try to hide this from his voice as he spoke. "When you see this you maybe now understand why I am not so worried about school dinners or too bothered about the showers in my dormitory."

Toby remained mute; his brain completely overwhelmed by the cacophony of stimuli it was being assaulted by. Chenna was happy to continue his commentary.

"This is a good place, my friend. Do not think you are looking at poverty Toby, these people are lucky, they have homes, jobs, food, schools and even a hospital. What you see here is what we had when I was little. You may not see the unlucky ones, the ones who have nothing. They live outside of towns like this. They do not know if they will eat today, they live every day like it might be their last, but not in the way we mean when we say it."

Toby suddenly felt very humble, very proud and very grateful to have a best friend like Chenna.

The zoo crates had been stacked at the front of barge meaning they would be unloaded first which was courtesy of the colonel who had ensured that the Port Authority placed the precious cargo on last; a special treatment that usually required a position of power or a generous bribe to achieve.

As the crates were being unloaded Micha was the first to wake and was quick to offer low pant-grunts that served to calm her family as they slowly came round and were able to pick up the first scents of their new home. For Sundance, Daphne and Cindy these smells were hardwired into old, almost forgotten memories of childhoods spent free and wild. For Kianza, Micha and Sally they were new experiences but still somehow managed to offer a sense of familiarity, a genetic memory switched on for the first time. Achilles was the most confused. His home had been the dry plains of north Africa, closer to his zoo home in south east England than this jungle wilderness that was as alien to him as it was to Toby and Dan. But still, there was a primal sense of calling that was pulling Achilles back to a former life, one that he had all but accepted he would never see again. For almost all of the occupants, the crates suddenly offered an intolerable barrier to a freedom so close they could touch it.

To Sally, however, the container was fast becoming a sanctuary, a final line of defence against her fearful imaginations of a land best left unexplored. She had sunk as deep into the corner of the crate as its cramped conditions would allow and had drawn up her nest vegetation around her like a security blanket.

Due to the presence of Dr Mbaeri and the orders of the colonel the crates barely touched the ground of the docks. They were loaded straight onto the waiting trucks, two on each and were ready to for the five-mile journey to the sanctuary. It was an hour-long trip on dirt tracks that saw them thrown around like socks in a tumble drier for the entire time.

By the time it was over the Potters, Dr Mbaeri, Chenna, Jack and Natalie stepped down almost as one from the three trucks and broke into a spontaneous cheer when they saw the wire fence gates to the chimpanzee reserve.

The smiling face of Dr Dagoa, Chief Veterinary Surgeon and Ethologist, head of the Chimpanzee Conservation Centre and only Congolese national to play rugby for both Oxford and Cambridge University was welcoming them in from the other side. He threw open the gates and gave a roar of laughter on seeing his old friend, team mate and colleague Jack Friday. Dr Dagoa could not resist ducking in towards Jack for a mock rugby tackle before embracing him with a heartfelt hug and three solid slaps on the back to drive the message home.

"Jack, Jack, Jack my friend. Ten years since I have seen you and you still look like you could be in school. How is it possible that you have not aged a day? Is life so easy for you?" Dr Benedict Francois Gabin Dagoa, spoke without breaking his smile, his eyes glistening with delight at seeing his old college friend and rugby captain.

"BFG, The Big Friendly Giant, how are you doing? It is so good to see you, Frank. Life has been hard for you I see: it looks like it is forty years since I saw you last." They both laughed and stood shoulder to shoulder as they turned to face the other travellers.

"Please, please, come on in. We must get these most precious of travellers out of their crates and into some comfortable surroundings. They can sleep here with us tonight and then we can begin the trek to the sanctuary island tomorrow where they will begin their rehabilitation for real."

The trucks carrying the company of soldiers had joined them, and the unloading operation began straight away. The captain was under orders to assist in any way necessary and then to take up a position guarding the facility from the perimeter, and he executed these orders with a level of precision and discipline that made Dr Mbaeri beam with pride. The six crates containing the chimpanzees were moved to a fenced enclosure to the side of the main hospital compound while Achilles was transferred to a separate enclosure further inland in an area partitioned off with electric fences and a deep, water-filled moat. This area was generally used for any injured leopards to recuperate in, but fortunately, it was vacant and free for Achilles to use as his overnight accommodation.

Frank Dagoa led his guests through the compound and up the steps into the main building that served as the animal hospital and guest accommodation. The vast white panelled hallway revealed the home's colonial heritage. A throwback to the days of immense wealth and exploitation by the Belgian government as it sought to plunder as much as it could from the vast lands it had stolen from the inhabitants.

Jack, Natalie and Toby had no interest in spending one second away from the crates as they were unloaded, and the occupants released.

Sundance was first out of the crate and made straight to the nearest tree and scaled it to the very tip, hooting deep throated whistles and barks that told the world around that he was back and was going to be in charge very soon. Kianza followed him out but did not dare climb right up next to his father, sensing that any such claim of matched status would not have gone down well. He settled for a branch a few metres below but joined in with the calls, higher pitched but just as joyful.

Micha had emerged more slowly than Toby had expected and stayed close to her crate, resting a hand against it, as if she was afraid to let go, scared it might disappear as soon as she turned away from it. She finally released her grip, like an astronaut letting go of the rocket to begin their first spacewalk. Cautiously she crept towards her mother, gentle pant-grunts signalling to her that all was OK, they were safe, it was all right to leave her steel cage to see it all for herself. Eventually, it was the smell of fresh cut fruit that enticed Sally out as Jack and Natalie had served up armfuls of papaya, mango and breadfruit with chopped sugar cane mixed in as a special reward for coping with such a terrific journey. The food brought Daphne and Cindy to the clearing and summoned Sundance and Kianza down from their perches as well. It was late afternoon with sunset only two hours away at most. All six chimpanzees wanted to eat and to make nests in their crates for one last night of capture.

Jack and Natalie, kept an eye on them until they had all nestled down for the night and would have stayed on watch for longer had not been for the commotion in Achilles' enclosure where the mighty lion had been expressing his displeasure at his surroundings since making his first paw step back onto the continent of his birth.

The sedatives and twenty-four hours in a hard-floored metal box had left Achilles feeling groggy and grumpy and in no mood to be left in a muddy paddock with a few scrubs and thorn bushes dotted around an otherwise barren field. He was tired and hungover which left his roars sounding more like mournful meows than the regal rantings that he was aiming for. Jack and Natalie could do nothing to calm him as he paced furiously around the enclosure and could not hide their humour every time he stumbled, the medication still working its way out and giving him the look of an indignant drunk lost on his way home.

In the end Toby, Jack and Natalie left their animals to the night air and returned to the hospital.

"Ah, the workers return, come in, come in, my

friends. How are your precious beasts? Do they feel at home? For they surely are home."

"Thank you, Frank, thank you for all you have done for us, Natalie and I will never be able to tell you just how much this means to us, and to Toby. You have made our dreams come true."

"Oh Dr Friday, you are making me blush. Come join us for dinner, and you can whisper in my ear how much you love me."

Frank roared with laughter at his suggestion and pulled a chair in close ready for Jack to take his place next to him.

Natalie had felt a certain unease outside and needed to be close to her friends. The soldiers had finished unloading the crates earlier on and had set up their base camp outside the perimeter fence as ordered. She had watched them from the enclosures and was uncomfortable with the looks she was getting from them and could not shake a feeling that they were being held captive rather than protected by their guards.

"Please, please, sit and eat, my friends. We must eat plenty tonight as we have a long trip tomorrow to the sanctuary where we will spend the next two nights. I have some guests there who will be very pleased to meet you; Jack, I have such a surprise for you, I cannot wait to show you."

Frank was like an excited schoolboy but refused to divulge any more before they reached the island.

Chapter 31
Sanctuary

Jack did not have long to wait to find out who Frank was so excited about. The Sanctuary Island was actually part of the sprawling complex, an offshore two-hundred-acre jungle island that was home to the other animal guests at the reserve, a small colony of bonobo apes.

The colony of thirty apes had been rescued from an area of forest destroyed by fire further along the coast and had been living on the island for just over a year. Frank was incredibly proud of his resident bonobos and could not wait to introduce them to Jack and Natalie.

The Sanctuary was technically not an island as it was joined by a thin spit of land on the south side of the river. The Congo River at this point in its course is over three kilometres wide and was perhaps one hundred metres deep. The island jutted halfway out into the river and ran parallel with the shore for just over two kilometres and was half as wide at its widest point. It was covered in dense vegetation with the central area comprised of jungle fauna while the shoreline was carpeted in tall, thick grass that grew to over two metres high in places. The spit of land that joined the island to the main shore was ten metres wide at its narrowest point, and the gated fence across this portion formed the only barrier between the animals and the outside world; once on the island they could roam free, unencumbered by human interference.

The plan had always been to introduce the chimpanzees to the wild in this slightly controlled environment, so they could be kept under observation for the first month. Achilles was coming too but he would have a fenced off area of his own at the far end of the island until he was ready to be moved downstream to the Apex Predator Project. In this early period, they would have ever reducing human contact, until they had been seen to be able to survive entirely on their own. Once they could do this, Micha and her family would be moved to their final destinations deeper inland, deep inside in the vast Maringa Reserve where, hopefully, isolation and the almost impenetrable forest would keep them all safe from their greatest threat — the presence of man.

The night they arrived all of the travellers had been ready for an early bed. Jack and Frank had shared a beer and swapped stories from their college days, but neither of them was willing to take it any further than that first drink. Dr Mbaeri and Dan continued their oddest of double acts, The Mountain and the Molehill as Natalie had dubbed them, out of earshot of Dan, obviously.

Dan spent the bulk of the evening giving Dr Mbaeri

the benefit of his views on civilisation and, where possible, the Doctor patiently tried to correct them.

"Of course, you can never 'ope to tame this sort of place. That town we just came from is proper Wild West stuff, no law 'n' order, no infrastructure, just tin huts instead of mud huts, innit?"

"And tell me, Mr Potter, what happened to the Wild West? Is it not California now?" The minister kept an unbroken charm offensive throughout all of his conversations with Dan as if winning this one vote was vital to his campaign to change his beloved DCR.

"You are thinking in the wrong timescale Daniel, my friend. If you look at America, there were people alive to watch the moon landing whose parents would have been alive at a time when they were robbing the land from the Native Americans. So much change in a century from horseback to high rise in just over a lifetime. I do not expect to be the man who changes the lives of the people you saw yesterday, but I can be the man who starts the change. When Chenna's children are grown, and even the memories of you and me have turned to dust, that is when the changes will be seen, one tiny step at a time."

The conversation at breakfast followed along similar lines.

"I get why you want to help your countrymen but why are you so bothered by the chimps, why go to all this trouble for some monkeys?"

"Mr Potter! I hope Toby cannot hear you saying such things," Dr Mbaeri showed mock horror at the words Dan was using to describe Micha and her family. "I cannot save my country and destroy it at the same time. The time for thinking that just one species matters are over Daniel; Toby knows this, and so does Chenna. Their generation has no problem thinking on a planetary scale, but you and I are still stuck in our old ways, the ways that have brought us to the cliff edge. It will be their generation and the next that will save us, so long as we do not drive us all off the cliff before they get their time at the wheel."

Dr Dagoa joined the conversation.

"Our minister is quite right, Mr Potter. These few chimpanzees may be a tiny symbol now, but if we are to establish a way of preserving this country and developing it at the same time, then it will be because of what we learn here, on days just like today. We must work towards a realisation that the

true value of a tree or a forest is when it is standing, not when it has been cut down Mr Potter. This rainforest that surrounds us is big enough to protect and feed us all but only if we let it live. And it cannot truly live without the animals that live within it."

Fortunately, Toby had not stayed to listen to his dad disrespecting his ape cousins. He had headed over to join Micha and the rest of her family, using the time to go over what the day had in store for them all.

He explained, through Micha that they need to go back into their crates but only for a few hours. The news was received better than either of them expected. Sally was already back in hers, and Daphne and Cindy were happy to have another sleep after their breakfast. Achilles surprised them by getting straight back in his crate when asked, mumbling the whole time about being taken back to the zoo if they did not find him a better location.

The soldiers had stayed on the perimeter the whole night and worked with incredible efficiency and skill to load the crates and ready the trucks for departure. Dr Mbaeri was amazed at how the soldiers completed their tasks with such precision and with seemingly no need for verbal orders from their captain. The minister was used to seeing such highly trained soldiers in the capital, around the government buildings but these were nothing like the, hungry, hollow looking soldiers he typically encountered in the jungle outposts. Usually, when he met troops out of the big cities, they were barely in the same uniform and often could not march together, but this unit was nothing like that. The captain and his company were strong, highly trained and well equipped. Dr Mbaeri assumed the colonel was putting on a show for him, but Natalie still could not shake a feeling that the soldiers were not there just for the good of the chimpanzees.

It was mid-morning when they set off for the

Sanctuary which was much later than Dr Dagoa had wished for. The delay was

due to necessary checks being carried out on Achilles who appeared to have injured one of his front paws, no doubt during his stumbling huff the night before. He was not in the mood for Natalie or Jack to check it, and in the end, they were forced to sedate him again which they were reluctant to do for risk of him injuring himself further. It was as well they did, however, as he had sustained a deep cut and had a thorn buried deep in between his toes that could easily have become infected.

The drive to the Sanctuary was less than five miles but still took the best part of two hours to complete in the heavy, uncomfortable trucks.

When they arrived Dr Dagoa unlocked the gates guarding the spit of land to the island and directed the trucks to a very rudimentary compound found in a clearing a few hundred yards into the dense rainforest. There were already a few heavy-duty canvas tents that were semi-permanent and a makeshift hospital hut used to stabilise any injured animals before they could be moved back to the main hospital back at the conservation centre on the mainland. The campsite had a small fire burning and pot of stew on the go which let everyone know that there was at least one other human on the island.

Once again, the soldiers made quick work of

unloading the trucks and this time split themselves into two units, one to assemble new tents for the travellers and one to set up a perimeter patrol to safeguard them all within the compound. Dr Mbaeri and Chenna were given a very regal looking tent that would not have looked out of place in a film about the days of the Raj, which embarrassed him greatly and made him beg Dan and Toby take it instead. As the tent was big enough to house a small circus it was agreed that all four would share it.

The plan had been to take Achilles to the far side of the island, to the grasslands, but Jack decided to delay this for twenty-four hours, so he could check on his wounded paw. It meant another day in the crate for the mighty beast, but Jack knew that it would be far more challenging to manage the situation if the paw became infected after Achilles was released. It was agreed that it was safe to leave him sleeping in the crate while they went to oversee the release of the rest of the animals.

Once the tents were up and the equipment stored away the crates were fitted with shoulder poles that were used by the soldiers, four men per container to carry them for the thirty-minute trek to the centre of the island where the chimpanzees were due for release. Toby walked alongside Micha's crate and told her that the Humans would be staying in the camp and that food would be brought out to them at this drop off point for the first week to ensure that they had enough to survive while they adjusted to their new way of life.

Jack had explained this bit to Toby and had told him how important it was that they all resisted the temptation to keep contact going with any of the chimpanzees after their release. They needed the animals to regain their instincts and wanted them to be free of human contact as quickly as possible. Natalie had been there when Jack discussed this with him, and she had stayed to comfort Toby after he was gone, knowing how hard it was going to be for them to let their magnificent Micha leave their lives.

Once they reached the release site, Dr Dagoa was acting like a man possessed, unable to control his excitement at the importance of such an event.

"My friends, my friends, honourable minister, children, great army warriors, come in come in. We are here. Here is the end point of your mighty journey. This is where your beautiful chimpanzee companions must take their first steps to freedom."

Dr Dagoa was bobbing from side to side, somewhere between an involuntary twitch and the nervous pacing of a prize fighter waiting for the bell. His arms swung about him like they were acting on a whole separate set of instructions from the rest of his body and his head was bouncing up and down, dodging blows from an imagined opponent but all the while his smile had grown to a point where it had endangered the stability of the rest of his head.

"Should we say a few words for them before the release? Perhaps 'fly my pretties'."

Frank squealed with delight at his comic suggestions but could not bear to delay things any more, and signalled for the release to begin. The soldiers opened the crates simultaneously so that no occupant got stressed at being left until last. All of the occupants except Sally were much quicker to emerge from their boxes this time, with Micha edging it slightly by being out first and able to make it to the pile of cut sugar canes that had been left as an enticement, for any feeling more timid about their release.

Sally had taken up her usual spot in the far back corner of her crate; bedding leaves pulled up over her as if she wanted to be forgotten about and left to remain in the crate for the return journey back to the zoo. Micha sat patiently in the doorway, her hand holding out a sugar cane like a baton in a relay race, ready for her mother to take it from her. She kept up a slow, steady hum of low huuhuu sounds as she sought to reassure Sally that it was, again, safe to leave the crate and join them on their exploration of their new home.

"Come out, Mum, please come and eat with us. We need to be all together. We need to find a place for the night and search out

what food there is for us to live on."

"I don't want to explore; I don't want a new home. I don't want to look for food. I had a home, one I didn't need to explore and one where the food came to me, not the other way around." Sally was rocking back and forwards as she spoke, her arms wrapped around her pulled up knees, the body language of a frightened human child so perfectly matched in this mature, mother ape.

Micha needed all of her patience and the persuasive powers of Daphne and Cindy, but after almost an hour Sally emerged from the crate, rushing to the safety of her female clan as she did. By the time she was out, Sundance and Kianza had already checked out an area ten times the size of their old zoo enclosure and arena. They had climbed each tree and had called out to each other, loud, triumphant whoops and barks, chanting like victorious football crowds from one treetop to the next; the surrounding jungle hearing these sounds for the first time in over a century, so long had it been since chimpanzees had lived wild in these parts.

Once news spread that Sally was out, Sundance and Kianza returned to earth, and all six huddled together as the figured out what to do. A chimpanzee colony is far from being a democracy, but Sundance knew he could not fight all three mature females at once so needed to get at least one of them on his side so the troop would be forced to follow him.

The plan was made for the family to move to Sundance's new spot when a strange human walked into the clearing with an even stranger looking ape walking alongside her. Annabelle Jones, the island's resident paleoanthropologist had come to meet them and had brought the alpha female bonobo, Kiki and her son Kalala with her.

Chapter 32
Huu Hee?

Kiki and Kalala kept a slight distance behind Annabelle and did not, at first, enter the clearing, preferring the safety of the trees while they assessed the situation. Both they and Annabelle had been attracted by the commotion Sundance and Kianza had been causing since their release and had been keen to check out the new arrivals.

The importance of this meeting had certainly not been lost on Annabelle, or Dr Dagoa, who had been discussing it since plans for the relocation had first been discussed many months prior. Both knew that contact between bonobos and chimpanzees in the wild was incredibly rare and had only really been observed in zoos and circuses over the past few decades. Before this time, bonobos were largely unknown to the scientific community. Annabelle Jones had been studying them for six months, hoping to learn about how early humans might have lived.

Toby, Jack and Natalie had spotted the trio as they approached the outskirts of the clearing and Natalie was almost unable to control her excitement. It took every ounce of her professionalism and experience to stop herself from running straight over to the visibly timid animals.

"Oh my god, Jack, Toby, look! Bonobos! I can't believe it. Wild bonobos! Almost no one ever gets to see them in the wild. We are so lucky."

"Bonobos? What are they?" Toby hated to display such a glaring lack of knowledge like this, but he had no idea what he was looking at

"Bonobos, Toby? You know. Pan paniscus, our other cousin. Pygmy chimpanzees, as they used to be called until we realised they were a different species entirely. Chimpanzees and bonobos are more closely related to us humans than they are to gorillas, mate." Jack made no attempt to hide is excitement.

"Humans split from chimpanzees and bonobos almost seven million years ago, but bonobos and chimpanzees did not split from each other until about two million years ago, when this mighty river you see here cut through this land and divided the colonies of their common ancestors in two. Gradually the species grew apart, unable to cross the river to meet again to carry on breeding as one species. Almost like two lovers caught on either side of the great divide." Jack was getting quite carried away with himself. "Mind you, there was a case early last century where a male bonobo was sold to a circus as a chimpanzee and got put in with a load of chimpanzees. It was reported that they could still cross-breed, as some baby bonobozees were born! But in the wild, they never meet. Well, not until today, that is."

"The amazing thing is, the two species have ended up like mirror images of each other," Natalie added. "The chimpanzees are male- dominant, aggressive societies that settle disputes through violence, whereas the bonobos are female-dominated, peaceful apes. They rarely fight and almost never kill each other, and settle their disputes with lots of kisses and cuddles.". From a look she shot Jack at this point, Toby suspected that kisses and cuddles didn't quite cover the whole topic being discussed.

As Toby listened, he felt a familiar furry hand reach out for his as Micha joined him. She stared in wonder at the approaching apes, her first sight of relatives that she never knew she had.

Both Kiki and Kalala held their position on the outskirts, with the larger, alpha female keeping her son partially hidden by her position. Like all bonobos, they both appeared as a slender, more graceful-looking version of a chimpanzee, smaller but no less muscular. Their faces were flatter and rounder than those of their cousins, with their long black hair parted in the middle of their foreheads. Toby could see that their legs were much longer, a fact that became apparent as soon as Kiki stood to face them, straightening her back fully as she did. Her stance was much more upright and human-like than a chimpanzee, her body curved more like a human as well. Her hands were gentle looking with fine, dexterous fingers that would not look out of place skimming the keys of a piano or wearing gloves in an operating theatre. Her slim upper body and longer neck all added to the illusion of her being a stepping stone in the evolutionary pathway, somewhere between chimpanzee and human, but not belonging entirely to either group.

Kalala looked to be a recently mature male in perhaps his mid-teens, and was keen to impress the others with his position as the first son of the alpha. He kept his position just behind his mother, partly a nervous defence against these unknown intruders but mostly out of fear of reprisals from his mum if he tried to upstage her. He stayed on all-fours. Again, the position showed the difference in the bonobos' physique as his back was flat and parallel to the ground, while Kianza, who mimicked the new boy, showed the familiar muscular chimpanzee stance with sloping back and shoulders, like a powerlifter preparing for their next clean and jerk.

As Jack and Natalie headed back into the clearing to gather cameras and microphones ready to record whatever happened next, Micha risked a whispered question to Toby. "Who are they? They are like chimpanzee, but not like. Do they belong to you?"

"No, no, they are nothing to do with us. I don't know who the woman is, but the animals are bonobos, our nearest relatives apparently."

"Well, we had better go and say hello then, hadn't we?" Micha gave a gentle but insistent tug of Toby's hand that told him he was either going to follow her or risk losing his arm at the elbow.

As they walked towards the visitors, Micha began to chant a series of gentle huu-huu sounds, just loud enough to be picked up by the bonobos. It was more like a conversation that she wanted them to overhear, than a loud call aimed directly at them. Toby still had no idea what the syllables Micha was saying actually meant, but he knew that he was listening to a language that conveyed a great complexity of messages. Micha's family, in return, were calling out to her in a mixture of pants, grunts, huu-huu coughs and shrieks. They sounded to Toby like a mixture of encouragement, warnings and advice, with the usual threats from Sundance thrown in for good measure.

It could not have been more than fifty metres from the centre of the clearing to the edge, where the bonobos were, but Toby and Micha took two minutes at least to cover it, Micha keeping up her monologue the whole time. As they grew closer, Toby was reassured to see the welcoming smile of Alice beckoning them on and had not heard any cries from behind him forcing him to head back to camp. Once they had halved the distance between them, both Micha and Toby could hear the very soft replies from Kiki, a series of high pitched hee-hee sounds that seemed, to Toby's ears, to mimic the rate and rhythm of Micha's calls. Toby did not doubt that Micha and Kiki were talking with each other, and from their open, relaxed faces, it looked to be a friendly chat. They both knew they were too close to Alice to risk open conversation, but Toby gave Micha's hand a tight squeeze, seeking rather than giving reassurance. Micha responded with a smile and a nod that told him the chat had gone well and it was safe to proceed. As they crossed the final patch of dry grass and scrub that lay between the two groups, Alice knelt down to face the two newcomers.

"Hello there. Who do we have here?"

"I'm Toby, and this is my friend, Micha. She is one of chimpanzees that we have brought to live here."

"Oh my, you are the Toby Potter I have heard so much about. Jack's young protege. Dr Dagoa has told me all about you. I am Annabelle Jones, I work here. This is Kiki. She is the oldest female in the group, and this is her firstborn son, Kalala. They belong to the colony of bonobos who have been living here for the past year. We came to see what the commotion was about, but I am guessing it was all from the magnificent-looking hunk sat over there."

She looked at Sundance with a sense of awe, mesmerised by his intensity and physicality, both of which he had turned up to eleven. He was crouched low, by the exposed roots of a tree, with a Hulk-like stance.

His muscles were tensed, hair fluffed up, and eyes buried deep beneath his creased brow. The contrast between him and the two bonobos could not have been more stark: brooding malevolence meets serene acceptance.

While Alice and Toby were distracted, Micha slipped his grasp and edged towards Kiki, her head held low, and posture softened to show great respect to the older stranger. Kiki's expression relaxed further to show Micha there was no threat and held her hand out, palm up, in a classic begging gesture that was common to all three species of ape present. Micha made her way forward on all fours and came to a rest, sitting just an arm's reach from Kiki. She was close enough for them to touch as she reached out to take the waiting palm. Their fingertips brushed gently against each other, and both laughed, lips peeled back and heads raised, a nervous giggle between two curious and excited women.

Kalala was hopelessly out of his depth, not knowing whether to show strength and charge the stranger or stay back and respect his mother. In the end, he settled for some flexing and posturing of his arms and shoulders while rocking on his feet, but stayed in a low crouch to keep all options open.

"I am Micha, daughter of Sundance. We are chimpanzees who have travelled far to be here. These No Hairs have brought us here so we can live freely, in a world without fences."

"You are welcome, Micha. The jungle is our home, and now it is your home as well. There is much jungle here."

The two females moved closer to one another and embraced with a kiss and quick groom that served to calm them both further. When they were close enough to whisper, Kiki spoke softly into Micha's ear.

"Beware of the ones you call No Hair. They bring great pain. We have a different name for them here. We call them Mbaya Tumbili — Bad Ape."

"Yes, we know they can bring much harm, but the ones that you see here have helped us. The little one, Toby, is my friend. The others have brought us across many worlds to get here."

"A few are good, but many more are mbaya sana, very bad. We have heard many, many bad things on both sides of the great water. Chimpanzee and bonobo are brother and sister, split by the water but joined by our fear of the Bad Apes. I saw you talking with the little one. Does he understand our language?"

"No, he does not know what we are saying, but I can talk to him in his language. Toby says we were all brother and sister once, but the humans lost their hair and left the jungle. I do not believe him. Why would anyone lose their hair?"

"You are clearly a very special young lady, Micha, but you still have much to learn. Don't worry. I will teach you."

Kiki and Micha were already too deep in each other's company to notice that Jack and Natalie had crept closer and, after a nod of approval from Annabelle, had started filming the ape meeting. Toby and Annabelle had moved to the shade of a nearby moabi tree, its familiar umbrella crown jutting out above the canopy.

The heat of the jungle sun had left them soaked with sweat and too drained of energy to do anything about the flies that engulfed them. The afternoon clouds had begun to gather, and the pressure cooker humidity was reaching boiling point. If the rain fell early then, there would still be enough heat left in the day to turn the jungle into a sweltering sauna, but if it held off for an hour or so the inevitable shower would offer them a cool evening and keep the flies away until well after the evening meal was finished. Toby had not yet learned to read the signs of the weather, but he felt that if it did not cloud over soon, he would have to stay in the shade where he was until nightfall.

Jack and Natalie seemed unaffected by the heat. They were so engrossed in filming Micha and Kiki's first meeting that they stood transfixed in the clearing, taking a direct hit from the tropical sun as it crossed from its midday triumph into its late afternoon decline. What feeble breeze there was seemed happy to stick to the upper levels of the jungle canopy high above them, concentrating on making the occasional leaf flutter but showing no interest in cooling anyone down on the ground. Most of the soldiers had taken a break from the ferocity of the heat for an hour or so, resting on makeshift beds or lying under the shade of the trees, but the gathering clouds and a slight lessening of the afternoon furnace blast had encouraged them to return to work. With an unspoken cue, all of the soldiers rose to their feet, picked up their guns and headed into the clearing to await orders from their captain.

The soldiers appearing in the clearing had an immediate effect on the bonobos. Kiki threw her head up and stood at her full height, suddenly oblivious to her new friend, all thoughts focused on the influx of armed men. She shrieked an alarm call to Kalala, who had already taken to the trees, calling out a reply to his mother. His voice was full of fear and urgency.

"Mbaya Tumbili! Quick, Micha, come with us! Bring your family, we must hide!" Kiki wrapped her arm around Micha and pulled her towards the shadows of the trees, all the while calling out to all who could hear.

"Bad Ape, Bad Ape!, Follow us, follow us!".

Sundance, Daphne, Cindy and Kianza did not wait to hear any further explanations. They bolted across the clearing, knocking Natalie roughly against Jack as they charged to the safety of the forest, following the trail of their new guides. Bonobos, happiest in the trees, made

267

for the canopy as quickly as they could. Chimpanzees, who usually preferred the ground, followed on the jungle floor for the first few yards before joining the others high in the upper branches.

Only one chimpanzee remained behind. A terrified and confused Sally rushed back to her crate and closed the door behind her as she buried herself beneath the remnants of last night's nest.

Jack and Natalie looked around, bewildered at the explosive flurry of activity, at a loss as to explain what caused it.

While the travellers were looking around in confusion, Dr Dagoa was able to offer an explanation. He made his way over to Jack and Natalie to fill them in. "Well, that happened a bit quicker than we planned, but I would say your chimpanzee party has been released back into the wild, Jack. Well done, Captain, your project is a success." Frank patted Jack on the shoulder and then rested his arm across it.

"The bonobos are here because their home was destroyed by developers looking to extend mining operations further into the jungle. The army help with these operations, and I believe they shot two of the troop during the clearance. Apes have incredible facial recognition, you know? Way better than you might think. My guess is that the two who were just here will have recognised some of the soldiers and were not willing to wait around to become target practice again.

The chimpanzees will have responded to the bonobo's panic and followed them."

"They certainly left in a rush. But they are back where they belong and our mission is complete, even if they didn't stop to say goodbye." Jack smiled at Natalie as he said this and gave her a gentle hug. She smiled back up at him and then, to both of their surprise, kissed him, holding him in an embrace that paused time and, for a brief moment, stopped the world from spinning.

As ever, Dan was confident that there was no mood or situation that could not be improved by his shouting. "Oi oi! What's goin' on 'ere? Looks like two became one. Jack and Natalie just became Jackalie."

It never really mattered if anyone else laughed at his jokes, as Dan always did enough of that for everyone anyway. Jack and Natalie broke their embrace and looked around at the group sheepishly. They shuffled awkwardly from side to side before becoming engrossed in desperately urgent and important tasks like putting lens caps on cameras and rearranging tripod stands, both acting as if nothing had ever happened.

Toby looked on from the shade, where he had been stood all along. He hadn't moved or spoken since the apes had left. The slow realisation that Micha had gone was starting to gather momentum, until it hit him like a speeding truck. His amazing friend had left, and he might never see her again. As the impact of the blow played out in his head, Toby only just noticed that the rains had begun. The dry mud paths and centre of the clearing were fast becoming mudslides and pond-sized puddles. His dad ran to him and sheltered him in his coat as they headed back to the others ready for the hike back to the camp.

Such was the haste with which everything was loaded that they were well on their way back to camp before her first shrieks from the crate told them that Sally was still in hers. When Jack checked her he could see that she was in an intense state of distress. Her head was tucked low to her bunched-up knees and her arms wrapped tightly around them as she rocked violently, knocking her shoulders on the crate walls as she did. Her cries gradually reduced to whimpers, and she refused to look up and face Jack, no matter how much he called to her.

By the time they made it back to base, it was clear that he was going to need to sedate her, as they had no other way of getting her out of her crate to assess her for any injuries. Dr Dagoa tried to bribe her out with a beautiful platter of sugar cane, guava and garcinia, a delicacy that the locals called monkey fruit, but Sally would not so much as lift her head from her knees to acknowledge it.

In the end, Natalie administered a sedative dart, and Jack and Frank lifted her into the hospital hut where they could check her over. The rest of the gang headed over to their tents and the camp fire, ready for a meal and a rest, blissfully unaware of the far greater storm that would hit them tomorrow.

Chapter 33
The Last Supper

By the time Jack and Natalie had attended to Sally and Achilles, it was almost dark, and the offer of cold beer and hot stew had not meet with any resistance from either of them.

Annabelle Jones had joined them on the walk back to camp, keen to share her findings and immerse herself in some much-needed human company.

The stew that Annabelle had left to cook on the low heat of the smouldering campfire all day had fed the rest of the group already and they were sat on the benches staring at the embers, thinking of the events of the past few hours when Jack and Natalie came to join them.

Chenna and Toby were exhausted from the day's efforts and were struggling to stay awake by the end of the meal. The adults had a little more energy left in them, and all were enjoying hearing about what Annabelle had been doing for the past six months. As usual, it was Dan who had led the questioning.

"So, what's the story with you and these bobos then, Annabelle? Are you just good friends or is there something else goin' on?"

Dan always worked on the assumption that a cheeky smile and a wink could help him get away with most comments, no matter who he was talking to; he was usually right. Annabelle laughed and replied.

"Oh gosh, I'm not sure we're even good friends." Annabelle was one of the few people left on the planet who still used the word 'gosh,' but it just seemed very natural when she said it. "I think I am just an uninvited guest that they seem to tolerate, well most of the time they do." Annabelle had not really had much in the way of conversation for the past six months and did not need a second invitation to talk about her beloved bonobos.

"They really are the most beautiful creatures I have ever seen. We spend all our time looking at chimpanzees to find an explanation for our violent ways when we should be looking at bonobos and finding explanations for our softer side. They really can tell us so much about ourselves; it is scary to see how alike we are but also how desperately unalike we are as well. When we want to be, we are so, so much more violent than chimpanzees could ever be. We kill more freely, torture, imprison and oppress others on a scale that would make chimpanzees recoil in horror."

"Steady on Annabelle," Dan interjected. "Toby has been tellin' me about his beloved chimps. They kill their babies and they hunt and eat other monkeys; they bash their brains out when they do it. Not sure we do that sort of thing very much."

"Really Dan, do you never hear of step-parents killing their adopted children in the news? We may not hunt our food much now, but we have turned whole species into factory commodities, enslaving their children, so they never see the light of day and killing them the moment they leave their mother's teat. Have you been to an abattoir Dan? Have you seen how we dispatch our prey? It is not any prettier than the way chimpanzees do it. We have just got more efficient at doing it, and better at hiding it."

Annabelle felt herself getting a little flushed as the attention had become so concentrated on her, but she was on a roll now and saw in Dan someone in need of having their views challenged.

"But not only are we so much more violent than chimpanzees we are also so much more loving than bonobos when we want to be at least. Bonobos are the most affectionate animals I have ever seen, but on any given day we can be more sensitive and compassionate to others, even total strangers than a bonobo has ever been. The difference in the power struggles of both types of ape, tells us so much about ourselves as well. Chimpanzees are male-dominated, and it is the alpha who gets all the ladies. But it is never the case that one ape is so strong that he can be in charge all by himself, he will always need allies, so the alpha male is often not the strongest but the best at making alliances, usually based on threats and intimidation. Alpha males rarely last for more than four- or five-years tops; they just can't maintain the threats, no matter who is backing them. Bonobos though are female dominated, and their alpha can last a lifetime, and bonobos never kill their children Dan. They don't use violence to intimidate others into getting power; they use... umm" She paused and looked at Toby and Chenna, suddenly not sure if you should take this chat any further, a blush on her cheeks managing to show through her sunburn nicely. Toby came to her rescue. "Kisses and cuddles?" he offered as a suggestion.

"Ooh yes, that's it lots and lots of kisses and cuddles. Bonobos gain their control by sharing affection and by sharing with those around them."

"So, they shag their way to the top then, yeah?" Dan could carve his way through to the middle of any debate, no matter how edifying, using crudity as his guiding light. As ever the comment got the laugh he was most after, his own.

"Ah, I think my friend Mr Potter has hit upon something," spoke Dr Mbaeri. "I am loving the intrigue of the political world of these apes, Miss Jones and as ever it has come down to the only two possibilities — you can either wield power to control sex, or you can use sex to control power! The apes have ended up with the same systems that we have!" The minister roared with laughter at his observation, and Dr Dagoa matched him in effort and volume.

"Well yes, I suppose, in a way you are both right. But the real point is that not only are we more violent than chimpanzees but we can also be more loving than bonobos, better at sharing, more altruistic, far, far better at building communities than they could ever be and so much kinder to strangers than they are. It is not surprising that in a world dominated by male scientists we have concentrated on the importance of alpha males. The view for the past fifty years has been that violent competition is in our genes, it is just who we are. But if all we had ever done was research bonobos for this time, we would not be saying that at all. Our success in conquering the world has made us think that we are all that matters. The apes do not burn down the forest where they live, but we do. They don't poison their rivers and destroy the foods they rely on, but we do. They do not kill off every animal they get a taste for, but we do. We keep examining animals to see how alike us they are when what we really need to do it study them, to see how unlike us they are. We need to understand that every other animal that has the capacity to think and to love and to be successful and does so without having to destroy the world it lives in. As far as we can tell we are the only living creature on Earth to ever live this way, so completely out of touch with our natural surroundings. Maybe we should try and learn from the rest of the animal kingdom, while they are still with us."

Alice paused, looking down at the plate in front of her

as a wave of desperation crested over.

"God if only they could talk to us. Hopefully, some of us would be smart enough to understand what they were saying?"

Toby and Natalie cast each other a guilty look and Toby, especially, suddenly thought that maybe they had done the wrong thing in keeping Micha's gift a secret.

"Do you think Micha and Kiki were talking to each other today when they met?" Toby knew the answer to his question, of course, but he wanted to know where Annabelle was with this.

"Toby, you know the answer to that," Jack answered before Annabelle could speak. "I've told you that animals can manage only very basic calls and instructions to one another. Complex conversation like we are having is one of the things that separates us from the rest of the world's inhabitants."

Annabelle was quick to give a reply to Jack's assertion. "Oh Jack, that's a bit anthropocentric for these enlightened times, isn't it? Every time we have tried to find a quality unique to humans, an animal has come along and proved us wrong. Cognition, mirror tests, Theory of Mind, tool use, empathy, compassion, you name it we have been wrong about it. Virtually every animal on the planet has a similar nervous system, and every large mammal has a similar brain yet we are certain we are the only ones to have developed language? Really? Would a safer assumption not be that they do have language, but we are yet to understand it? Does an elephant who can transmit infra- sounds over miles that can be heard by their feet through vibrations in the ground really not have a claim to having a better-developed communication system than us? Whales calling to each other over hundreds of miles of ocean? Are they really just giving alarm calls? Of course, they can talk, Toby. With what we know about the similarity of mammalian brains and the way they respond to the same stimuli why would we question that? Is it because science tells us so or is it because, as Darwin said, that when we enslave animals it makes us very uncomfortable to think of them as equals?"

"That's because they're not equal; we're 'uman and they're not, end ov." Dan liked to feel that any argument could be resolved by finishing your sentence with 'end ov'.

"But Dad they are equal, equally important at least. They feel the same way we do, love their family like we do, they suffer when we hurt them like we do. They've been on the planet longer than us; they are faster and stronger than us and live longer than us. The only thing they don't do like us is to try to burn down the planet."

"How do you know they love their families like us or suffer life us? No one can know that for sure."

"Well, if anyone can, Toby can. He has spent more time with Micha taking her around the zoo than any of the rest of us." Natalie felt the need to defend her co-

conspirator and like Toby felt a need to confess. "I am sure that animals have their own languages; it's just that we can't hear what they are saying yet. Maybe Toby will be the one to crack that code for us."

"But Miss Jones you forget one thing. We, humans have a soul; the animals do not. Surely this is why we are not equals? When we kill an animal, it is not worried about Heaven and Hell, it just dies. We, humans, have much more to worry about, so our suffering is greater." Dr Mbaeri spoke with such depth of voice that Toby wondered if this was what it was like for elephants when they hear with their feet.

"I am sorry, Minister, but I cannot accept that view. We can either have evolution, or we can have souls, we can't have both. If a soul is unique and eternal and indivisible, then it could not have evolved. Evolution requires gradual, random change over countless generations. We cannot have had humans with a bit of a soul, not if they are eternal and indivisible. And plenty of us humans do not worry about Heaven and Hell. When we kill an animal for food, or clothes or fun. It would rather live and if we wound it first it suffers, not because it is worried about eternal damnation in Hell but because it wants to be out of pain and back with its pack or family."

"Ah my beautiful guests, this has been a most educational dinner has it not? But I fear the day has taken its toll on me, and I see Toby and Chenna cannot keep one eye open between them. Maybe we should make our beds, for tomorrow we must leave early to head back to the release zone if we have any hope of ending Sally's suffering and reuniting her with her family."

No one had the energy to fight Frank's suggestion, and all were keen to head to their tents to rest and reflect on an incredible day.

Chapter 34
Bad Ape

Natalie could sense that something was wrong the moment she woke up.

She had risen early to check on Sally and Achilles, but when she emerged from her tent, she was struck by such an immediate and total sense of isolation that for an awful moment she felt that she had been left as the only one in camp. Once she had gathered herself, however, she was able to spot what had changed; all the soldiers had gone. Natalie looked around in bewilderment. How could they have slipped away without making a sound, without waking anyone?

She was about to call out in alarm when she saw Jack closing the gate to Achilles' makeshift enclosure where he had just finished checking the lion's paw and making sure he was comfortable.

Distracted by the site of Natalie he stopped what he was doing with the lock and called out to her as she stood there in her jungle shorts and white vest.

"Morning, Lara Croft, you off on an adventure somewhere?"

"All the soldiers have gone, they've taken

everything."

Jack did a sudden scan around the camp, noticing his surroundings for the first time that morning.

"Oh god yeah, you're right. We better tell the minister; he might know what's going on."

They did not have to wake Dr Mbaeri to tell him as he was stepping out of the mighty tent along with Chenna and by both the Potters. He had spotted what had happened before either Jack or Natalie could say a word.

"Where are the soldiers? Where is our transport?" The minister spoke with the authority and sense of entitlement that comes from being someone who is not used to getting let by down by either.

"We don't know; we thought maybe you would."

"They were under strict orders to remain with us throughout our stay and escort us back to Kisangani tomorrow morning. I will radio the colonel now and will expect their return immediately."

Dr Mbaeri showed incredible acceleration for a man of his size and seconds later was barrelling through doors of the hospital hut just as Frank was coming out to join them, beaming his trademark smile. The reason for his smile could be seen clutching his left hand as Sally had joined him and was walking alongside, relaxed and happy looking, holding a piece of her beloved sugar cane in her other hand.

"Look who is joining us today. Sally is feeling in a

much better mood. I think she likes being in the hospital more than in the jungle. The good news we have for her is that we do not need to take her to find her family for they have come to collect her."

Frank pointed to the back of the hut where the jungle almost touched the walls to show everyone that Micha and Sundance had led the family back to find Sally and had brought at least another half dozen bonobos with them. The chimpanzees were sat on the ground but the bonobos, feeling less comfortable in these surroundings, had stayed in the trees. All except Kiki who was sat next to Micha, deep in conversation again. Even Dr Mbaeri stopped his charge to look at what Frank was showing them. For a moment his concerns about the soldiers left him, and he was just happy to take in the splendour of what he was seeing.

The moment of calm lasted no more than five seconds, and the speed at which everything happened next left the whole group stunned and unable to function as minutes compressed to seconds and seconds stretched to hours.

Sally never heard the bullet that hit her and was slumped on the ground, the sugar cane still hanging from her mouth before Frank could so much as let go of her hand. The beautiful chimpanzee lay motionless and bleeding, her limp arm hanging from Frank's grip as if it was trying to pull him down out of harm's way.

The gunshot echoed around the compound, panic

surfing on the sound wave as it crashed over humans and primates alike. Dr Mbaeri reacted first, his thoughts only for his son as he breached the twenty metres across the clearing in what seemed like two giant strides. He engulfed Chenna, Toby and Dan, smothering them with his huge frame and knocking them to the ground as he did it. Frank dropped down beside Sally, instinctively checking for any signs of life from her limp body while Jack and Natalie both sprinted for cover behind the transport crates crouching low, each sheltering the other. Only Toby thought of the apes.

"Micha! Run! Run, get out of here. Ruuun!"

His words were wasted on Kiki and the rest of the bonobos who had launched themselves high into the canopy, screaming alarms calls to each other as they went. Daphne, Cindy and Kianza had likewise retreated deep into the undergrowth, but Micha had frozen to the spot, her eyes fixed on her fallen mother's body.

All of the non-human primates had fled the camp or were rooted to the spot in terror. All but one. If anyone had taken the time to notice Sundance's response, they would have been left in some doubt as to which to be more afraid of, the gunshot still echoing around the campsite or the expression of murderous rage that had locked the mighty ape's face into a mask of fury.

Despite the intent etched on his face, Sundance's movements following the shot were as measured as they were malevolent. He stepped back slightly into the shade of the tree trunk beside him and dug his heels into the dirt as he did. Slowly he leant forward on to his knuckles as a sprinter would when steadying himself against the starting block. His eyes deepened into their sockets, leaving them looking like the dark chambers of a shotgun barrel. His sights were aimed beyond the clearing, focusing hard on the band of heavily armed militia who had swaggered into camp from the east. The gang members each had rifles slung over their shoulders where the barrels rubbed against ragged tee-shirts. Well-dressed gun belts hung like medals around their chests in grotesque contrast to the torn and threadbare football shorts and ill-fitting trainers that made up the rest of this military charade.

The warriors strolled to the centre of the compound with a leering confidence that showed they were no strangers to making such an entrance, used to paralysing their victims with fear, indifferent to the suffering it caused.

At their head was the oldest of the troop, a tall thin knife blade of a man whose face was crisscrossed with fine scars that showed the map to a lifetime of conflict and battle. His left eye was covered with a patch that had the head of a lion etched across it. Down his right arm snaked a thick band of vivid pink keloid scar tissue that ran like a lava flow from his shoulder down to his wrist. His left arm hung casually across a heavy machine gun that could have sat comfortably on the top of a tank or the deck of a small frigate. His gold-toothed smile lacked any sense of joy or kindness and flashed, instead, like a warning of the dangers that lay ahead.

The rest of the gang were no more than a mix of teenagers and children. Their guns and knives looked like lurid fancy dress costumes, but their lifeless gazes and humourless faces told a very different story. From a distance, they could have looked like pupils following their teacher on a trek, but up close it was clear these were the foot soldiers of a vicious and accomplished warlord. To anyone who took the time to notice, it would also have been evident that the leader was the focus of all of Sundance's attention.

The armed gang took their place, centre stage as the stars in their own private theatre of war. They stood in silence and waited for their audience to acknowledge their presence.

The leader of the gang spoke first. "Ladies and gentlemen, I hope I did not startle you when I ordered my breakfast a moment ago". He pointed to Sally's lifeless body as he spoke, punctuating his comments with a short bark-like laugh that gave no sense of any humour.

"My name is Mjambu Milandu, but you can call me Jam. In Swahili, my name means 'survivor' which as you can see is certainly true." His left arm traced the side of his face and down his right arm, giving a guided tour of the highlights of his most obvious disfigurements. "I am also the rightful ruler of this territory that you are trespassing on. You may not know who I am yet, but you will soon..." Dr Mbaeri did not let him finish.

"I know who you are. You are the Butcher of Bondo, and these are the wretched children you have enslaved and dragged down into your godless sewer." The minister was on his feet as he finished speaking, inflating his frame to its maximum extent, casting a shadow across the clearing as he did. He had locked eyes on his adversary and did not once flinch from the stare that he was met with.

Mjambu showed genuine amusement at the minister's words, responding with a respectful nod. His child entourage merely let their expressions sink to ones of weary resignation, knowing as they did that any such defiance was always met with appalling acts of savage brutality in return.

The oldest of the gang was seventeen years old, the youngest nine. Between them, they had witnessed and perpetrated so many atrocities that they knew a speedy, painless death was the best that any of their captives could hope for now.

"My word, we are truly blessed to have such an honoured guest amongst our band of trespassers." Mjambu turned to his gang, relishing his ringmaster roll. "Step forward my brave men, come and see our very own Minister for Health, Dr Mbaeri, The Man Who Would be King, here in the flesh." He swept his arm in a full arc of the arena as he spoke, stiffening his body into a mock stand to attention. "And what flesh there is boys, we will not go hungry for a month!" This time his laugh was genuine but lasted for only half a breath, the rest of it being used to bark out terrifying orders.

"Axe and machetes only on the big man." A venomous leer snaked across his face as he uttered these words. "Ntambe keep your gun on those two boys if anyone moves shoot their legs off. If the minister resists, do the same to the women. We are going to take our time skinning the good doctor, I think. Start low and work our way up boys, no need to rush this job."

His words drew the breath out of each of the captured and terrified guests.

Toby and Chenna stood motionless, crying silently, the trembles from Dan's hands running through their chests as he continued to hold them tight. Natalie and Jack had no idea if they had been spotted or not but were crouched behind the crate fighting terrible cramps in their thighs as they tried to stay still below the line of sight. Frank was clinging to Sally with his hand pressed against a cavernous wound in her side. Not one of them had dared make a move against their attackers, not one of them had any attempt at a plan.

Except for Sundance.

Each of his movements had been minuscule but

combined they had seen him move behind the tree where Micha stood so that he could climb it unobserved leaving him able to cross to the roof of the hospital hut and over to the left of Mjambu, keeping to his blind side the whole time. In all his manoeuvring Sundance had not once taken his eyes of his quarry. The face he saw burned deep into his memory, waking childhood images that he had tried every day to forget. The face that Sundance saw in front of him was the face of the man who orphaned him and sold him off for meat all those years ago. All he needed now was a moment to strike and almost thirty years of rage and regret would find the escape they had been looking for.

He did not have long to wait. Mjambu was keen to get started and had already removed his sabre-like machete from his belt and was using both hands to lift his unwieldy canon from his left shoulder.

The moment the leader of the gang stooped to lay the gun down Sundance saw his chance. With both hands momentarily trapped under the heavy weapon, one locked around the machete handle Mjambu was at his most vulnerable. The boy, Ntambe, tasked with keeping his rifle on Chenna and Toby had his back to his leader, and the rest of the gang had already lowered their guns and brought out their knives in preparation for their ghastly task. Sundance took all of these details in and reacted to the opportunity with astonishing speed and horrendous intent.

Releasing an atavistic roar Sundance made two enormous leaps to clear the distance between him and his prey. Mjambu had time only to jolt in surprise, and half turn his head, trying to get his right eye in position to show him what was happening. His efforts were of no consequence. Sundance was upon him in a second and had lifted the machine gun buy its barrel, swinging it effortlessly, like a child's toy, as he lifted it high above his head before bringing it down axe-like on to the back of Mjambu's neck.

The force of the blow shattered the butt of the gun against the ground sending a shower of splinters and dust around the collapsed body. The noise of the impact masked the quieter but equally brutal sound of Mjambu's cervical spine separating as the fatal blow put an end to his time as a 'survivor'.

The speed and ferocity of the attack caught all of the boy soldiers entirely off guard, but they too had survived many attacks and were veterans of countless battles, so it did not take them long to regroup. Ntambe was swinging his rifle round to face Sundance, and the rest of the gang had dived for the ground, recovering their guns with well- practised ease. Within seconds the child soldiers had formed a tight, heavily armed group facing a bunch of terrified defenceless men, women and children who had never once been into battle; the militia knew the odds were heavily stacked in their favour.

Sundance saw his greatest threat came from

Ntambe and was trying to close the gap on him before the rifle could be brought to aim. It was clear that he was not going to make it and all of those on his side stood in helpless despair waiting for another shot to ring out.

But no shot came.

Instead, a roar rang out, a cry that had not been heard in this part of the jungle for more than twenty years. Achilles was free from his compound having cleared the unlocked gate, left open by Jack in all the confusion, racing to the sound of the commotion. Two days of sedation and meagre rations had left him hungry and angry, and the burst of energy he felt in his short sprint had made him feel more alive than anytime he could remember. His legs felt the thrill of the hunt again, and the muscle memory knew what to do. He spotted the gang of boy soldiers and raced in low and fast, ready to split the heard and single out his target.

The child soldiers had fought many terrible battles in their short lives, but not one of them had ever seen a lion before, never in the wild and never charging them at full speed. Their screams froze, lodged in their throats as Achilles launched himself on to them knocking all five of them to the ground, guns and knives flailing, their weapons rendered useless by the terror that had paralysed their limbs.

Only Ntambe remained focused, his weapon raised but uncertain where to aim. The moment of hesitation as the barrel swung from Sundance to Achilles gave

Sundance the time he needed to reach Ntambe unharmed. His rage had not lessened after the killing of Mjambu, if anything it had grown, and Sundance knew with deadly certainty that Ntambe was about to suffer the same fate. He grabbed the barrel of the gun and wrenched it from the hopelessly outmatched boy and begun to swing it with the same murderous intent as before.

Ntambe was a second from death when a voice sounded out; a voice that until that day had been heard by only two people ever before.

"NO!"

Micha bounded into the centre of the arena, on all fours but her head up, so her words had the best chance of being heard. "Don't kill him, please don't kill him."

She reached Sundance as he was raising the rifle on its upswing and used all her weight and strength to resist her father's efforts.

"Please don't kill this boy, there has been enough killing today. They have killed my mother; you have killed their leader. Please, no more. No more. Achilles, let them live."

The effect of Micha's words was like a tropical storm on a lit match. The flames of the conflict were suffocated by the enormous weight the sound of these words brought with them.

Natalie and Jack rose from behind the crates, Jack's mouth hanging open in disbelief, his eyes flitting between Micha, Toby and Natalie, a queue of questions fighting to burst through the doors of his mind like shoppers on the first day of sales.

Dan and Chenna were unable to process any of what had just happened, and Frank was torn between his efforts with Sally and the staggering nature of the events unfolding before him. Ntambe dropped to his knees and burst into tears, his nine-year-old self, surfacing to show his true age for the first time since he was orphaned and captured by Mjambu two years previous. He was lost in a frightening new world where his monstrous father figure lay dead in front of him, and a talking chimpanzee was deciding his fate.

"I'm hungry, why should I let them live?" Achilles had his front paws on the chest of two of the fallen soldiers and was eying the others, daring them to try and make a move. His words spoken in the common language were meant for Micha and Sundance.

Sundance replied: "I want to kill the boy. He is like all the other No Hairs. We should kill them all before they kill us."

Micha spoke in a mixture of chimpanzee, common animal tongue and human as she struggled to keep hold of the situation.

"We must not kill the humans; we must teach them. It is not their fault that they do what they do, they are sick. Kiki explained it to me. Humans and apes once were one. But the Humans separated from us long ago.

At first, it was OK. They lived like us in the jungle, and we were still brother and sister. But soon they began to lose their hair and forgot how to climb. Then the river came, and chimpanzee and humans went to one side and bonobos in the other. Chimpanzee and humans lived together for a short time before the sickness came, but after that the No Hairs could not live with us any more. Their heads swelled, and they forgot how to speak with the rest of us. They could not climb or talk like us; they could only talk to each other. Their heads got bigger as the sickness got worse. They started talking to things we could not see and hearing voices that were not there. These voices told them to do terrible things to each other and to all other animals. They left the jungle and did not return for too many moons to count. But then they did come back they were sicker than ever; they hear so many voices now, some many messages telling them they are special and the only animal that matters. They fight each other if the voices tell them to but still no one but them can hear these voices. They live here now, but they hate their jungle home and everyone who lives in it. They try to destroy it all because they have remembered where they came from and it shames them. We must teach them, show them how it was before they became sick. We must tell them how to live as we do again, sharing the world around them. We must show them that we are brother and sister, teach them how to speak with us again, remind them how we must live —

one planet one species."

Micha was exhausted by her efforts of translating from chimpanzee, to human, and to the common language. She could feel her grip on the gun barrel weakening and could sense her father's hold strengthening. Achilles' claws were out and had begun to dig into the boys' chests. She could tell her words were not working, she needed help and looked to her closest friend to get it. Toby broke free from his dad and ran to Micha the moment she turned to him. He rested his hand gently on hers but made no effort to wrestle control from Sundance. Instead, he faced him and spoke gently, nodding at Micha to let her know to translate what he said.

"Your daughter is right. We have forgotten where we came from and who we are. But she can teach us. For the first time, there is an animal who can lead us back. If there is more killing now then maybe we will all die, and if Micha dies, then our best chance of saving the planet dies with her."

Sundance looked at his daughter, again, with a sense that he was seeing her true self for the first time. He lowered his gun and gave a cursory grunt in the direction of Achilles telling him to stand down, let his prey live.

Just when Ntambe felt that his hold on reality could not get any weaker, he watched through tear-blurred eyes as the bushes and undergrowth of the jungle around the compound rose up and walked into the clearing. The soldiers missing for the morning had returned. Swathed in dispersion pattern material and covered in camouflage paint and foliage from head to toe, the platoon marched back into camp from the perimeter snare that they had formed around the clearing.

Dr Mbaeri was first to grasp the full picture of this morning's events.

"An ambush? An ambush with me, my son and all my friends as bait? Are you out of your mind captain? They could have killed us all."

"Not at all, Minister. There was a minimum of three sets of crosshairs on each of these bandits from before they walked into camp. We could have put them down at any moment if we needed to. We have been tracking Mjambu, that monster, for months now but could not get close. He has been terrorising local villages up and down this stretch of the river for over a year, killing without mercy. We knew he would not resist a chance to take some hostages, so we saw you and this little spit of land as the perfect opportunity for a trap. We had hoped to take him alive so we could put him on trial in Kinshasa but I see that this soldier got to him first." The captain smiled with respect at Sundance.

"Your career is over Captain. It will be you who goes on trial."

"My orders come from very high up, Minister. I do not think we will be troubling the courts at all today."

As if to confirm his claim the sound of helicopter blades reverberated up the river signalling the arrival of the Colonel and a cohort from the President's personal security unit.

"I assure you, Minister; you were all under my supervision at all times. No one would have got within five metres of you and lived."

Dr Mbaeri suddenly felt too tired and too relieved to argue, he merely turned towards his son and broke down sobbing the moment he felt his touch.

Dan had been silent long enough.

"Would someone kindly tell me what the fu…"

With impeccable timing Annabelle rounded the corner of the hospital hut stopping Dan's expletive in its tracks. She was on her way back from the garage workshop that was kept out of ear shot from the camp to keep the noise from the generator motors to a minimum.

"Morning all, we have guests I see. Have I missed anything? I was working in the generator down at the river and thought I might have heard a shot…oh god what's happened to Sally?"

Frank and Jack were lifting Sally into the hospital hut as she spoke. Jack had confirmed that there was a weak pulse and they were rushing to see if they could stop the bleeding before her heart gave up for good.

Micha and Toby had left Sundance who had melted back into the forest. By the time Annabelle arrived, they were leading Achilles back to his enclosure, Micha holding on to his mane while Toby held her other hand. They were talking freely now with no secrets left to keep.

"Even out here the world will get to know about you Micha. They will not let you live in the wild. They will keep you in a lab like they did with your dad."

"I don't mind. I had to stop the killing. Do you think my mum will be okay?"

"If there is any chance of saving her Jack will do it. He is an amazing surgeon and so is Dr Dagoa. They will do everything they can. I promise."

"I know Toby. I know you No Hairs are not all bad."

"Oh gosh. I could have sworn I just heard Micha speak. I must be losing my mind," said Annabelle.

"Don't worry Jolly Hockey Sticks; your marbles haven't gone anywhere. She's talking all right. And she just saved all our lives. And my boy has got a lot of explain' to do in a minute, believe you me."

Within minutes of Micha's intervention, the helicopter landed. They touched down in a clearing close to the river, and the Colonel entered the compound with his additional troops, just as the clear up operation was underway. The captain and his men had taken Ntambe, and the rest of the gang into custody using the transport crates as makeshift cells. Dr Mbaeri and Dan were talking with their boys, Toby bringing them up to speed about his incredible secret.

"I did tell you about her dad. The very first time she spoke I told you and Jack and anyone else who would listen. None of you believed me."

"Of course, we didn't believe you, you, doughnut. It was your mother's funeral. We thought you were 'avin' a what's name… episode."

"Natalie had known for years before me. She was the one who said to keep it secret. She didn't want Micha to be put in a lab."

"But she needs to be. She is unique. We need to study her," Dr Mbaeri spoke with the absolute certainty that all men in authority use, when they are trying to handle a situation they know nothing about.

"If I may make a suggestion?" Annabelle joined the conversation with her usual timorous reserve that gave no hint to the iron cored determination that lay beneath it. "Why don't we ask Micha what she wants, she seems to have proven herself every bit our equal, at least."

"The jungle is my home. I want to be here with my family. But humans are my family too. Can we live here with Kiki and her family? Maybe I can teach you and Frank. Perhaps that would be a start."

"Oh my. Oh, Micha. It would be an honour. Just think chimpanzees, bonobos and humans living together back in the jungle where it all began. Together again for the first time in two million years. Won't that be something?" Annabelle actually clapped her hands together and did a little skip when she said this.

"That's settled then. I will ensure this whole area has our full protection. Annabelle Jones, you and Dr Dagoa are tasked with saving the planet, Micha will tell you how to do it.. Once again central Africa will be the birthplace of humanity. But this time Humanity 2.0, the one that leads us back to our roots, back to the place of our birth." The minister was delighted with his words and with the chance to be seen to be doing something without actually doing anything at all.

Toby knew that the time had come for the goodbye that he had been dreading all along. The events of the last half hour had terrified him to his bones. He wanted desperately to be home, as far away from this jungle as possible even though that meant saying goodbye forever. Despite all his fears, Toby could see what Micha had become. She was all of a sudden, the alpha chimpanzee and alpha bonobo and just maybe the alpha human as well; she had put the ape into apex, and she was just where she needed to be. Toby could see that the mission had been a success and was certainly worth the sadness that he was feeling now. Micha had a chance to bridge a gap that humans had been building for a hundred thousand years, and he knew that this was too big a chance for anyone to stand in the way of.

Micha could sense Toby's sadness and felt it too. Silently, they both clasped hands and embraced in a tight hug, Micha's powerful long arms pulling Toby close, squeezing him like she was attempting some form of fusion of the two of them. With a constricted breath, Toby whispered, "I love you. I will remember you always my friend." Micha remained silent for a few seconds and then replied.

"I will never forget you, Toby; you are my favourite No Hair. I will tell my bonobos and chimpanzees that if there are humans like you, then we stand a chance, we can live together, all apes together."

As if to provide a stark reminder of just how much work she would have to do the Colonel joined the group accompanied by his captain.

"Minister. My captain informs me you have a talking ape. It is essential that we take it into our custody immediately, for its protection. There are many tests we need to perform. We cannot leave such a thing out here in the wild."

"A talking ape? I think your captain has been out in the sun too long Colonel. Maybe he has jungle fever. I am sure he needs some rest back in barracks or better yet at home with his family for a week or two. I seriously doubt that he wants to go to a tribunal to tell people about talking monkeys. He would be the laughingstock of the whole army." Dr Mbaeri fixed his gaze on the captain. "What do you say, Captain? Does two weeks home leave not sound like a better deal than trying to convince all your commanding officers about your talking ape story?"

The captain had been in the army long enough to spot a way out when it was being handed to him.

"Maybe I was confused Colonel; perhaps it was the children's voices I heard after all."

The minister took the opportunity to stand between Toby and Micha, putting his arm around them both. With flawless timing, Micha dropped to her knuckles and started rocking from side to side, shaking her head and panting out huuhuu sounds, occasionally throwing her head back and curling open her lips into a wild grimace to maximise her chimpanzee-like qualities. Dr Mbaeri, relishing in her performance, patted Micha gently on her back, signalling her to sprint for a tree which she scaled in seconds, vanishing into the canopy before anyone could raise a voice in protest.

"Excellent, we can put this whole event to bed. Now then Colonel I will be delighted to accept a ride for my guests and me back to Kisangani, we have planes to catch. Your men can break camp and return Dr Dagoa, Miss Potter and Dr Friday to the main hospital as soon as their patient is ready to be moved. Great things will be happening here, Colonel. When your captain returns from his leave you will need him to establish a permanent barracks at the main compound, we must protect this area at all cost: the future of the planet depends on it."

The minister did not wait for a reply from the bewildered colonel, he was heading for the helicopter, with Dan, Chenna and Toby racing to keep up. They were airborne and clear of the camp within two minutes, leaving it forever.

Epilogue

The journey back home to England went without a hitch. Dan and Toby stayed with Chenna and Dr Mbaeri for Christmas so the two boys could travel back together for the start of term.

Jack and Natalie stayed with Alice and Frank at the compound for another two weeks making sure that the new arrivals made a successful transition to jungle life on the island. Amazingly Sally survived her gunshot wound, but it was clear to everyone that she was far too traumatised to stay out in the wild. Micha and Jack agreed that she would be much happier back at the main compound, staying as a house guest with Frank, who would oversee her full recovery.

When everyone got back to England and life in the zoo got back to normal the transfer of animals back to the wild continued as planned. Omar and Selma made it back to the tiger sanctuary, and within the year Selma was a mother to three healthy cubs; Omar was not the father.

The animals that wanted to stay got to enjoy far greater space and Jack developed the hospital into a world-class centre of excellence for exotic animal surgery and rehabilitation. The TV cameras could not get enough of Dr and Mrs Friday, the most famous vet couple in the world.

Micha and the chimpanzees stayed close to the bonobos for many years with Annabelle astounding the world with her insight and research into ape's emotional intelligence. Annabelle visited the zoo regularly where her Planet Ark charity was centred. She always brought with her messages from Micha which Toby loved to receive. By the time he was ready to leave home for university to study Veterinary Medicine with his giant of a friend Chenna (who was studying law and politics), Annabelle had become part of the family, with Dan encouraging her to stay longer each time. Toby let his dad know that it was OK for him to fall in love again. Dan let Toby know that it wasn't OK for him to talk soppy like that to his dad.

On her last visit before university Annabelle brought the best news of all. Micha had paired with Kiki's son Kalala and the worlds first wild-born bonobeeze had arrived; an elegant, intelligent looking boy who walked upright almost as much as he crawled. He had said his first word at six months.

And what did Micha the Magnificent call her son?

Well, that was easy, I named him after my favourite No Hair, I named him Toby.

The End

305

Printed in Great Britain
by Amazon

85691037R00176